Contact Work Primer

**Edited by
Pete Sanders**

with contributions from
Catherine Clarke, Penny Dodds, Marlis Pörtner,
Lisbeth Sommerbeck and Dion Van Werde

PCCS BOOKS
Ross-on-Wye

First published in 2007

PCCS BOOKS Ltd
2 Cropper Row
Alton Road
Ross-on-Wye
Herefordshire
HR9 5LA
UK
Tel +44 (0)1989 763 900
www.pccs-books.co.uk

The Contact Work Primer

A CIP catalogue record for this book is available from the
British Library

ISBN-13 978 1 898059 84 4

Cover design by Old Dog Graphics
Printed by Cromwell Press, Trowbridge UK

CONTENTS

Pre-Therapy is entirely dependent upon the interaction between human beings. It actually makes a positive difference to people's lives. The seeds that were planted by Garry Prouty are now nourished, harvested and multiplied by the members of the Pre-Therapy International Network and many other people all over the world.

The Contact Work Primer is a *liber amicorum*—a book written by friends—and dedicated with respect, gratitude and affection to Garry and Jill Prouty.

FOREWORD

GARRY PROUTY

It is a pleasure to comment on the work of my colleagues: Catherine Clarke, Penny Dodds, Marlis Pörtner, Pete Sanders, Lisbeth Sommerbeck and Dion Van Werde, all members of the Pre-Therapy International Network. The Pre-Therapy International Network, founded by Jill Prouty in Amsterdam in 1995, was developed for academic, research and clinical explorations of Pre-Therapy. This book is an outgrowth of that very process.

Pre-Therapy as individual psychotherapy was born in the United States, and contact work for institutional settings was developed in Europe. This book reflects the development of contact work with a growing range of clients.

Catherine Clarke's essay on the IATROGENIC PSYCHOSIS of her son is a classic illustration of what can occur with 'brain-reductionism'—the belief system of a biological psychiatry. Pre-Therapy was used to help stabilize her son's emergence into family life.

The chapter by Lisbeth Sommerbeck is an excellent description of using contact reflections in the midst of traditional client-/person-centered therapy. It demonstrates 'following the process' of intermittent pre-expressive communications (the 'grey-zone').

Dion Van Werde offers an understanding of contact as a MILIEU therapy. It focuses on nursing practice which bridges pragmatic and psychological care, where contact reflections are applied both to ward structure and individual process.

Penny Dodds describes her work with nurses who provide primary care for demented patients. She articulates the important differences in using contact reflections with these organically impaired persons. In her second chapter she explores the process of teaching Pre-Therapy.

Marlis Pörtner has combined client-centered counseling and everyday care for people with various mental disabilities into what she calls 'Pre-Therapeutic Approaches'. The expansion of contact reflections to everyday care provides a therapeutic tool for caregivers in many situations. These situations can vary from opening a door, to emotional reactions to social involvements.

Pete Sanders introduces Pre-Therapy history and concepts, then writes a critical essay on the current nature of research methodology for counseling and psychotherapy. Within the context of statistically insufficient small samples, he reports that Pre-Therapy yields consistent and in some cases, sizeable improvements. This provides hope for further exploration.

He concludes with a brief look at current projects which point the way towards a positive future for Pre-Therapy and contact work.

Garry Prouty
Chicago, Illinois, 2007

CONTRIBUTORS

Catherine Clarke is a State Registered Nurse and State Certified Midwife, now working as a chiropodist. She has written several chapters and articles, and given presentations at conferences on carer issues in mental health.

Penny Dodds trained at the Maudsley Hospital in the 80s and then specialised in Older Persons' Mental Health. She is a Lecturer Practitioner working for both the University of Brighton and Sussex Partnership NHS Trust and is currently completing a PhD on the application of Pre-Therapy in dementia care.

Marlis Pörtner is a psychologist and person-centred psychotherapist working in private practice, with people with special needs among her clients. She is a consultant and trainer of staff members of social organisations in Switzerland, Germany and Austria. In her books she has developed specific person-centred concepts for different professional fields.

Lisbeth Sommerbeck is a psychologist accredited as a specialist in psychotherapy and supervision by the Danish Psychological Association. Her special interest is in the application of the person-centred approach with staff and inmates in the 'backyards' of psychiatry. She is author of a book and several articles and chapters.

Dion Van Werde is a clinical psychologist and person-centred psychotherapist. He coordinates the Pre-Therapy International Network and has translated Prouty's Pre-Therapy into a multidisciplinary ward philosophy and practice in psychiatric residential care in Gent, Belgium.

INTRODUCTION

Before we launch into looking at how contact with clients is centrally important to counselling work, it might be helpful to take a look at some definitions of counselling itself. It is important to locate the helping activity of counselling in relation to other helping activities in order to avoid confusion regarding the purpose of this book. Contact work is important to a range of helpers from support workers right through to psychologists, so this book is specifically aimed at two types of reader:

- people wanting to learn about contact work and Pre-Therapy with no previous experience or knowledge of counselling or psychology (e.g. care workers, support workers and nurses)
- professional helpers wanting a succinct summary of and straight-forward introduction to contact work and Pre-Therapy (e.g. counsellors, psychotherapists, social workers, psychologists)

What is counselling for?

One way of defining counselling is to look at what it is useful for. In the past thirty years, counselling has become ubiquitous, and perilously close to being presented as a panacea for just about everything. Some critics say that the emerging 'profession' of counselling has much to gain for claiming, on behalf of counsellors and therapists, that counselling *is* good for everything. It would be wrong, or course, to make such claims: counselling has its limits and part of being a counsellor is to know what those limits are. The problem is that when we are in distress, it is comforting to think that there is a simple answer around the corner.

The situation is not made any easier when we understand that simply sitting down and taking time out from a busy life can make things seem better. Counsellors must be able to explain to their clients the differences between this very important relief and comfort that can be gained from compassionate human contact on the one hand, and counselling as a specialist activity on the other. Counselling can help people in certain states of distress and usually involves change:

- change in the way the client sees things or themselves
- change in the way a client thinks about things or themselves
- change in the way a client feels about things or themselves
- change in the way a client behaves

Although many people will not be able to put it neatly into a few words, what they seek from counselling can be roughly summarised in a few categories:

- support
- problem-solving
- developing new strategies for living
- recovery
- gaining insight or self-awareness

The sort of distress that counselling can help is often called 'emotional' or 'psychological' and can include:

- stress—a very general and possibly over-used term, but there are some situations in life, especially those that you can't control, that might leave you feeling so stressed that it interferes with your everyday life
- conflict—at home or work
- bereavement—whether a relative or friend. Indeed, having anything permanently taken away might lead to a feeling of bereavement, such as losing your job or losing your ability to do something like walk, play sport or have sex
- depression—another over-used term and not one to be taken lightly. Many life events can make us feel low, and talking it over really does help. The popular term 'depression' can cover everything from feeling understandably low after having your purse stolen or losing your job, through to being unable to get up in the morning or eat properly because you think life is not worth living
- coping with poor health, e.g. having a long-standing health problem or receiving a diagnosis of a serious or terminal illness
- trauma, e.g. surviving (including witnessing) something very disturbing (including abuse of various forms)

What counselling is not for

When someone decides to attend counselling sessions, they are, by definition, distressed. It is, therefore, particularly important that the client doesn't have either their time wasted or their distress increased by attending something that we might reasonably predict would be of no help.

As we have already seen, it is difficult to honestly predict whether counselling will definitely help in a particular circumstance. Nevertheless there are times when counselling is clearly not the first or only appropriate INTERVENTION. It is doubly difficult to appear to turn someone away when they arrive because sometimes:

- part of their distress might be that they have difficulty feeling understood and valued
- they may lack self-confidence and a rejection would damage it even more
- they have been to other types of helper and they think that counselling is their last hope
- they are so desperate they might consider suicide

However difficult it might be, we have to be completely honest with clients if we think counselling is not going to help. It would be wrong to let them find out after a number of sessions, after which they might feel that they are to blame for not trying hard enough. The use of counselling should be questioned if it is likely that their symptoms of distress are caused by:

- poor housing or homelessness   • poverty
- lack of opportunity due to discrimination or oppression

Problems of this nature are best addressed by social action. The counsellor as a citizen shares responsibility with all other members of society to remove these blocks to peoples' physical and psychological well-being.

It would be convenient if we could divide problems up into two neat categories; those of psychological origin (and amenable to counselling) and those of non-psychological origin (and therefore not amenable to counselling). However, there are some other causes of distress which, although they will not be *solved*

by counselling, will undoubtedly be helped by counselling in that the person concerned will be able to function better with the kind of support that counselling can provide. It may also be that the client experiences repetitive patterns of self-defeating thoughts and behaviour which renders them less effective in dealing with problems which do not have a psychological origin. It might also be that a person would be better able to challenge an oppressive system if they felt personally empowered, and counselling can sometimes achieve this. Such problems include those caused by:
- poor health (a physical illness or ORGANIC CONDITION)
- oppression and discrimination, including bullying
- living in an abusive relationship

Counsellors must be constantly vigilant to ensure that their work with a particular client or clients in general is not contributing to disadvantage, abuse and oppression by rendering people more acceptant of poor conditions, whether at work or at home.

> Psychologists must join with persons who reject racism, sexism, colonialism and exploitation and must find ways to redistribute social power and to increase social justice. PRIMARY PREVENTION RESEARCH inevitably will make clear the relationship between social pathology and PSYCHOPATHOLOGY and then will work to change social and political structures in the interests of social justice. It is as simple and as difficult as that! (Albee, 1996: 1131, cited in Davies & Burdett, 2004: 279)

What is 'personal growth'?

Counselling in the UK has become associated with what might be called the 'personal growth industry'. Self-improvement has been a feature of our society for a hundred years or more and includes such initiatives as the Workers' Education Association supporting the educational needs of working men and women. More recently further education has embraced more non-vocational courses and reflects the fact that as we get more affluent we have to attend less to the business of mere survival. We can turn our attention to getting more out of life and along with other self-development activities, improving our psychological well-being proves to be a popular choice. Furthermore, when people have a good experience as a client, they sometimes see that learning to be a counsellor could be a further step in self-improvement.

This 'personal growth' use of counselling contrasts with counselling as a treatment for more acute forms of psychological distress as listed on page 2 above. It is, however, no less worthy or ultimately useful. Fulfilled, happy citizens, able to put good helping skills back into their communities are an asset, not a handicap.

WHERE DOES CONTACT COME IN?

Practically every person-to-person helping activity, from personal care through to psychological treatment requires us to be 'in touch' with the person we are helping. If you are doing day-to-day social care, such as helping someone eat, it is respectful to know at least whether they are hungry and that they want to eat what is on offer. If you are offering psychological treatment you at least need to know how the person identifies their problems, or, if *you* are required to make a diagnosis, then *you* will need to clearly identify the person's symptoms. It is all too easy to make assumptions (maybe from our own 'theories', the patient's notes or from other staff) about what a person does or doesn't want, is or isn't experiencing, without making *contact* with *them*. This is contact work, and as we shall learn, the results can be very challenging.

The spotlight was turned on psychological contact largely as a result of the pioneering work of American psychologist and psychotherapist Garry Prouty. He developed a way of working with chronically withdrawn patients in institutional settings which he called *Pre-Therapy*. This book is, then, about Pre-Therapy and the ways it can be used to help restore people to a relationship with themselves, the world and other people.

USING THE GLOSSARY

You may have noticed that some words are set in SMALL CAPITALS. This indicates that the glossary on page 112 carries a brief definition and explanation of the term. The SMALL CAPITALS can appear anywhere in the texts, quotes, subtitles or index.

1

IN THE BEGINNING IS
PSYCHOLOGICAL CONTACT

BEING IN TOUCH

Most of the time, we assume that we are heard and seen; making sense to, and somehow affecting, the people we are with. It is, at the very least, frustrating to say and do things which are not noticed and in extreme cases it can lead to feelings of isolation. The flip side of this is when we are with someone who doesn't seem to want to communicate with us, or whom we can't understand. Sometimes a particular person seems to be behind a screen, difficult or impossible to get through to—they are present physically, but out of reach in a psychological sense.

Human communication, human relationship, is impossible when this connection is missing. In everyday life we take this connection for granted, only noticing it when it is absent. A person daydreaming, for example, is quickly and easily brought back in touch with us with a word or two, or gesture, and will often apologise or explain that they were 'miles away'. If they don't 'snap out of it' quickly, we soon think something is wrong.

This *psychological contact* is the basis of all human relationships. Indeed it is impossible to have, moment-to-moment, a relationship without it. Several approaches to psychology are founded on the idea that humans can make good quality psychological contact easily. More than that, many have argued that human psychology requires another human being in order to function—it is based on the idea, and actuality, of an 'other'. A 'self' only makes sense if there are other 'selves' out there to relate to. John Shlien wrote:

> The mind emerges through a process of communication. This involves social interaction on the basis of what Mead calls 'significant symbols' (usually words). A significant symbol is one that is 'reflexive', i.e. when it is used it *presupposes another* person … *Acknowledging the other is essential to the existence of mind,*

> from beginning to end. (1961/2003: 39–40, original emphasis)

And, on the specific subject of psychological contact:

> we speak of 'reality contact' for instance (to be without which fairly designates the psychotic state) … (Ibid: 40)

Furthermore, related to the therapeutic situation, he also recollected:

> Two colleagues have described to me their reaction to a hallucinogenic drug. Both were deeply shaken, both terrified by the sense of 'not being', and significantly, both wanted above all to have human contact with a person, or persons, who *must not leave*. (Ibid: 38, original emphasis)

William Whelton and Leslie Greenberg also explain:

> The type of contact that is called 'psychological' is the type of contact that a human self has with another human self. (2002: 107)

Margaret Warner suggests the following definition, again emphasising the self-to-self contact:

> [A] fundamental adaptation of the human organism that allows human beings to feel that they are meaningfully present [and there are varying degrees and kinds of meaningful presence] both verbally and non-verbally to themselves and each other. (Warner, 2002: 80)

It is not an exaggeration to say human beings cannot survive without psychological contact. An out-of-contact person—a totally cut-off person—will become PSYCHOTIC and soon die. Humans subjected to solitary confinement or sensory deprivation rarely survive intact. From the work of psychodynamic psychologist John Bowlby (1953/1965) with orphaned and fostered children (commissioned by the United Nations in the late 1940s), we know that human beings deprived of affection and the opportunity to bond with a caretaker during infancy grow up damaged.

Also standard fare for psychology students are the experiments performed by Harry Harlow (1959) who 'discovered' that monkeys denied physical and emotional contact during infancy grew up psychologically and physically damaged. He found that infant monkeys preferred a cuddly surrogate mother to one made out of bare metal wire, even if the metal 'mother' had food in the form of a feeding bottle and teat. He called this *contact comfort*. Furthermore, he noticed that the baby monkeys were more confident simply in the presence of the more cuddly mother, even when they weren't touching it. The baby monkeys deprived of contact comfort did not develop normally—some died—and the damage was irreparable.

Mary Carlson, at Harvard Medical School, one of Harlow's students, travelled to Romania after the fall of Ceausescu to discover that the children reared in similar circumstances grew up with analogous permanent behavioural and emotional problems. She confirmed that in order to be human we need to grow in a human *interactive* or *relational* environment. In the 1950s, psychoanalyst Donald Winnicott summed up nicely the intrinsic, essential relational nature of human beings when he stated that babies don't exist; only 'nursing couples', i.e., babies-and-mothers, exist.

Although psychologists have long known that certain types of contact are essential for development, 'normal' functioning and day-to-day living, *counsellors* and *psychotherapists* were happy to accept, without too much scrutiny, the presupposition that if two people were in the same room, roughly looking in each other's direction, then psychological contact could be *assumed*.

CARL ROGERS AND PSYCHOLOGICAL CONTACT

In 1957, Carl Rogers introduced his 'six conditions'[1] with condition number 1: 'That two persons are in (*psychological*) contact' (cited in Wyatt and Sanders, 2002: iii). Without this first condition being met, none of the other conditions were possible. These conditions were reiterated in Rogers (1959), where he

---

1. In his famous paper: 'The Necessary and Sufficient Conditions of Therapeutic Personality Change', Rogers (1957). Reprinted in Kirschenbaum & Henderson (1990).

explained that he originally wanted to use the term 'relationship' instead of 'psychological contact' in his 1959 chapter. He only used the term 'relationship' in the explanatory text. Compare the 1957 and 1959 writings:

> Contact. Two persons are in psychological contact, or have the minimum essential relationship when each makes a perceived or SUBCEIVED difference in the experiential field of the other. (Rogers, 1957, cited in Kirschenbaum & Henderson, 1990: 221)

> The first condition specifies that a minimal relationship, a psychological contact, must exist. I am hypothesizing that significant positive personality change does not occur except in a relationship.
>   This construct was first given the label of 'relationship' but it was found that this label led to much misunderstanding … the present term, has been chosen to signify more clearly that this is the *least* or minimum experience which could be called a relationship. (Rogers, 1959: 207)

In the light of the fact that he wrote hardly anything else about psychological contact, it would be a mistake to take Rogers' statements about psychological contact as the last word on the subject. The condition of 'contact' or 'relationship' was assumed and therefore, for many years, largely ignored by even person-centred theorists and practitioners until in the mid-1970s, when, as we shall see in detail in this book, American psychologist and psychotherapist Garry Prouty turned the spotlight on psychological contact. The fact remained, though, that without contact, none of the other conditions were possible, no relationship can exist, no therapy is possible.

QUESTIONS ABOUT THE NATURE OF CONTACT IN RELATIONSHIPS

Before we look at Prouty's work, it might be instructive to interrogate our own experience, rather than rely on assumptions. Most readers will be involved in some sort of caring work as part of a job or with a friend or relative. When reading the questions below, by all means think about the sort of caring relationships you have, but also think about ordinary 'everyday' relationships with people. Psychological contact is necessary for all human interaction.

Is psychological contact a binary condition?
By this I mean is it an 'on-off' event: is there either psychological contact or no psychological contact? Or …

Is psychological contact on a continuum?
Are there degrees of psychological contact from 'full' contact to 'minimal' contact? And where on this possible continuum might be Rogers' '*least* or minimum experience which could be called a relationship' (ibid)?

What is the threshold of contact?
And staying with the idea of the *least* contact, what is the minimal experience that Rogers speaks of? How much or how little contact needs to be there in order to be sensed?

What *evidence* for contact do we use—what are the indicators for contact?
How do you, the reader, know you are in psychological contact with another person? What cues do you use—both to signal you want to be/are in contact with another person—and look for in the behaviour of the other person to indicate that they want to be/ are in contact?

Are there any necessary and sufficient conditions for contact?
Do you need to be in the same room as the other person? Or can you make contact on the telephone? In correspondence? Or by email? Must one be able to *speak* to the other person?

Must psychological contact be reciprocal?
Can we only have mutual contact, or can one person be in contact but the other not? And must it be consensual—can we withhold contact, or avoid it? How might we do this?

Not really *answers*, but a start ...

When we ask the obvious question (of which the above are constituent parts) 'What *is* psychological contact?' the result is more questions than answers. But at least we are now giving the subject some attention, and all those interested in helping relationships can play their part, because theory is still in development.

Embleton Tudor et al. (2004), affirm Rogers' view and advocate a binary view of psychological contact when they write:

> [T]he meaning is clear. Client and therapist need to be simultaneously aware of each other before anything therapeutic can happen. So, two people, awake, and in the same room, are in psychological contact. Two people talking on the phone are in psychological contact. ... The contact Rogers is describing is not about feeling close to each other, or even about recognizing each other as human beings ... it is simply about mutual awareness of each other's presence. (p. 39)

On the other hand, Warner concedes, when describing Prouty's work, that 'contact can be viewed as a continuum ...' (2002: 79), and Rose Cameron, (2003), obviously an advocate of the notion of *levels* of contact, asserts:

> The importance of this [psychological contact] in counselling is, as Rogers says, so obvious that it hardly needs mentioning. What is very much worth mentioning, however, is that there are different degrees of psychological contact. The depth of contact is what makes the difference between a rather mechanical and lifeless therapeutic relationship and one that shimmers with energy and involvement. (p. 87)

Cameron goes on to describe and provide names for what she considers to be the four levels of psychological contact: basic contact (meeting the other person), cognitive contact (understanding the other), emotional contact (emotional closeness), and what she calls subtle contact or intimacy. 'Subtle contact' echoes other writings, such as Thorne, who might call this phenomenon 'tenderness' (1985/1991) and Rogers (in Kirschenbaum & Henderson, 1990: 137), who might call it 'presence'.

She makes further assertions regarding the nature of contact, some elaborations of Rogers' idea, stating, for example, that contact *is* mutual and that contact *is* consensual, i.e. both parties must give permission for contact, or must choose contact. Therefore, we are not indiscriminately available for contact. People can and do put conscious limits on psychological contact.

There are further dimensions of contact, of particular concern to therapists, which could be understood as the *length* and *breadth* of contact. What do I mean by this? In short I mean how the time spent in contact with a client is structured (are there 'sessions' and if so, how long are they?) and the range of what we might call 'contact activities' (*ways* of being in contact with another person). There clearly is a difference between, for example, the quality of psychological contact achievable in a one-to-one professional 'sessional' therapeutic relationship compared with that which is achievable in a therapeutic community. The limits of a regulated professional therapy relationship are soon passed when we play with time, social situations the activities of therapy.

Person-centred therapist Regina Stamatiadis introduced the concept of 'sharing life therapy' in 1990 when she described extending the situations in which the therapeutic conditions can be offered to the client. Using even the most restricted, binary and 'obvious' definitions of contact, this means that psychological contact can be made with a 'client' in many different situations not usually associated with therapy. Stamatiadis (1990/2002) described using body tools (touching, smelling, wrestling, walking), art tools (painting, sculpting, etc.), gift-giving, social and life activities (shopping, taking train journeys, cooking, eating, and prayer). She explored the nature of time in terms of unlimited sessions and the varying rhythms of therapy.

Louise Embleton Tudor and Keith Tudor (Embleton Tudor et al., 2004) also describe their own experiment in a variant of sharing life therapy, wherein they convened a therapy group in which clients were touched and held, the group also ate together and celebrated special occasions such as birthdays. Such projects clearly challenge us to explore and possibly revise our conceptions of how psychological contact might be conceived, understood and expressed in different modes and contexts of human relating.

Developments in communications technology bring further challenges to therapy practice and psychological contact. Although Embleton Tudor, et al. (2004) confidently assert that 'two people talking on the telephone are in psychological contact', we must address issues including two people corresponding in a live internet chatroom, or two people corresponding by email, mobile phone text message, or by letter. For example, a relationship conducted by email has certain features that are different from a face-to-face relationship: there are no face-to-face visual cues, the participants do not need to synchronise their communications, the speed of communication is flexible and adjustable. Yet psychological contact is possible in such circumstances. Consider the following correspondence, taken from a real relationship reported by Murphy and Mitchell (1998) in which a client wrote a note of thanks to a counsellor:

> In just our brief exchange of messages you have left me with a sense that you are a caring, creative, helpful, hopeful soul. This is hard to achieve in person, let alone in the imperfect world of electronic communication. Your warmth and humanity shine through the pixels on my screen, and come at a time when I need them most. For this I thank you and congratulate you. The irony is not lost on me that I find a true person in the virtual void at the same time as a doctor in my home county has given me short shrift. (p. 23)

If therapeutic change is possible in such computer-mediated communications, then 'relationship' is possible and psychological contact is, by definition, established. In other areas of social science (e.g., computer supported cooperative work (CSCW)) theorists use constructs such as 'social presence' and 'psychological distance' as relationship qualities transmissible by computer and CSCW academics explore the most complex of relationships including cooperation, conflict, attraction and love (Lea & Spears, 1995). It is clear that psychotherapy theorists still have much work to do in order to come to terms with what Garry Prouty calls the 'essential' condition for therapy; psychological contact.

2

INTRODUCING PRE-THERAPY

Pre-Therapy is a method for bringing people back into psychological contact who are normally 'contact-impaired' due to learning disability, PSYCHOSIS, dementia, terminal illness, or brain damage due to illness or injury. Such people seem 'beyond human contact', in vegetative or CATATONIC, AUTISTIC or otherwise non-communicative states. It can also be effective with people who are contact-impaired through states of high agitation and confusion. It is difficult if not impossible to assess such patients for diagnostic purposes, to ask questions and understand their everyday care needs, to engage in therapy and other negotiated activities.

Successfully making connections with such clients in order to engage in meaningful conversations has thwarted clinicians for decades. This has resulted in clients being psychologically and socially isolated and effectively trapped in their own world. However, Garry Prouty's natural flair for reaching through and making contact with such clients has been a major breakthrough. After over 20 years of working with clients suffering from REGRESSIVE behaviour and PSYCHOTIC experiencing, Prouty eventually OPERATIONALISED his expertise, and published the first integrated account of theory, method and research possibilities implicit in his work in *Theoretical Evolutions in Person-Centered/ Experiential Therapy: Applications to schizophrenic and retarded psychoses* (Prouty, 1994).

Pre-Therapy is a person-centred[1] and deeply respectful approach, restoring the essential psychological contact which is necessary for all people to engage in reciprocal relationships (Van Werde & Prouty, 2007). Most of the time, people experiencing a PSYCHOTIC episode are unaware of their individual functioning within the broad spectrum of psychological contact. Pre-Therapy

---

1. However, we shall see throughout this book that Pre-Therapy is a pan-theoretical method, useable by practitioners from a wide variety of theoretical approaches.

develops this awareness by introducing 'Contact Reflections' (see Chapter 3). These are the skills which carers, professionals and others can use to encourage people who are out of contact to get back in touch with a shared reality. Prouty explains how to help clients regain contact with themselves, their environment and others so that they are increasingly able to engage in the everyday activities of life. At the same time the tenacity and overwhelming nature of PSYCHOTIC experiences often begins to recede.

Prouty was concerned to point out that Pre-Therapy is what happens *before* therapy of the usual psychological sort can take place. It is not a *complete* therapy by any means, and can be largely thought of as preparation for therapy (although we will look at this issue in a little more detail later). When used to create a contact ward MILIEU (see p. 18 and Chapter 6), it creates the conditions in which PSYCHOSOCIAL INTERVENTIONS and other talking therapies can be effective, it makes diagnosis more accurate and can help TITRATE medication because patient–doctor communication is rendered more effective. In addition it restores day-to-day contact with living in many patients, thus potentially reducing the load on nurses and support staff.

Having said that, as more experience is gained in the practice of Pre-Therapy, it is becoming clear that some symptoms of PSYCHOSIS are alleviated, if not completely dissolved, when the patient is able to make good contact with a shared reality. The best explanation for this is that such symptoms, including, in some patients, agitation, hopelessness and depression, are at least exacerbated by, and may be the result of, the personal and social isolation which accompanies PSYCHOSIS.

Prouty's inspiration for Pre-Therapy originated in the work of Carl Rogers, Eugene Gendlin and Fritz Perls. In his own practice, and that of most professionals currently using Pre-Therapy, the therapeutic context is still strongly person/client-centred (e.g. Sommerbeck, 2003) and/or EXPERIENTIAL. However, it is true to say that Pre-Therapy is a pan-theoretical method. It does not offend the philosophy, theory or practice sensibilities of the major approaches to therapy, from PSYCHOANALYSIS to COGNITIVE THERAPY. Practically any psychological therapy professional can learn Pre-Therapy and use it as a prelude to their own therapeutic work, regardless of theoretical orientation.

In addition to its 'neutrality' with regard to therapeutic approaches, Pre-Therapy theory is Prouty's integration of PHENOMENOLOGY, EXISTENTIALISM, client-centred, GESTALT and EXPERIENTIAL theories (see, e.g. Gendlin, 1973; Perls, 1969). It resonates with many elements of contemporary psychology. More advanced students may explore some of these via the work of, for example, Daniel Stern (1985).

This is further evidenced by Prouty's wide professional connections. In 2002 he delivered the Frieda Fromm-Reichman Memorial Lecture at the Washington School of Psychiatry and in 2004 he was awarded a 'Lifetime Achievement Award for Pre-Therapy' by the Chicago Psychological Association. He was also elected President of the Chicago branch of the International Society for the Psychological Treatments of the Schizophrenias and Other Psychoses (ISPS).

Pre-Therapy has been acknowledged and embraced by practitioners from many theoretical approaches, simply on the basis that, in their experience, it works.

PRE-THERAPY THEORY IN A NUTSHELL

In Chapter 1 we saw how the concept of psychological contact as proposed by Rogers was a very broad brush idea; it didn't give any real impression of the detail of the signs and signals of contact between people. We can also see how important it is to have a clear concept of the quality of contact made between people, especially in circumstances where one of the people concerned might have problems making 'normal' psychological contact.

Garry Prouty (2001: 591) reformulated psychological contact as 'the lived, prereflective conscious experience of the world, self or other'. By which he meant that people in contact show behaviours which give evidence that they are aware of (a) the world around them; (b) their own moods and feelings; and, through their interpersonal interactions, (c) other people. Prouty called these behaviours 'contact behaviours' (see Chapter 3). Of course this is a starting point, and one of the continuing efforts in the practice of Pre-Therapy is to pay close attention to the client's behaviour; to look for any evidence of possible contact behaviours.

The second part of Pre-Therapy theory involves the helper-therapist reaching out to make psychological contact with the client. The specific ways of behaving which Prouty discovered helped facilitate better psychological contact are called 'contact reflections', and these are covered in detail in Chapter 3.

We will see, in Chapter 10, p. 106, that attempts have been made to develop a scale to measure contact behaviours (Dekeyser, Prouty & Elliott, in press). Such developments not only help in research to determine if contact reflections actually affect contact behaviours, they also help practitioners further develop their skills in observing and understanding clients' contact-related behaviour.

PRE-THERAPY AND CONTACT WORK

Rather than look straight away at how to do Pre-Therapy contact reflections, we will take a few moments to explore the contexts to which this work is best suited. Without understanding the contexts and clients, the 'how to do Pre-Therapy' might seem rather strange. As we shall see in more detail in the next chapter, Pre-Therapy moves straight to the absolute basics of interactions to establish contact with people. It is not 'normal' behaviour for a 'normal' interpersonal relationship. It is a special way of relating developed for unusual situations, namely, where one of the people has difficulty in making and maintaining psychological contact.

Applications of Pre-Therapy and contact work

Garry Prouty's original work was done with people who were chronically withdrawn, CATATONIC and/or REGRESSED—the people with whom no one could work; consigned, usually for life, to the back wards of psychiatric hospitals. Since then, other applications have been developed in a variety of settings and more will surely follow. Below, we will distinguish between *Pre-Therapy proper* and *contact work*, and each has its particular applications, but for the moment here is a list of 'contact-impaired' people with whom

Pre-Therapy methods may be used to help restore, strengthen or sustain contact:
- people in a state of severe PSYCHOTIC withdrawal, CATATONIA or REGRESSION
- people suffering from DISSOCIATIVE states
- people with learning disabilities which impair communication and contact, from mild to severe and enduring
- people suffering from dementia
- people suffering from a terminal or degenerative illness which impairs communication or contact, including those, for example, whose palliative care causes drowsiness due to pain-killing drugs
- people with temporary contact impairment due to an ORGANIC CONDITION
- people suffering from a brain injury or damage

The principles of Pre-Therapy can be used by *all* staff and carers supporting and working therapeutically with such patients and service users. However a distinction is made between *Pre-Therapy proper* and *contact work.* The former, Pre-Therapy, is when a highly disturbed and chronically out-of-contact person is worked with to bring them back into contact as a *preliminary to therapy*. Contact work, on the other hand, is where the insights and methods of Pre-Therapy can be integrated in a more general way in communication skills of carers, nurses and support workers. Such people are not preparing their relative, friend or client for *therapy*. They are facilitating the restoration of contact to help with day-to-day living and personal care. Of course, this does not preclude preparation for therapeutic engagement, but it is not necessarily the prime aim of contact work.

A contact MILIEU

Whilst Pre-Therapy and contact work are effective in facilitating one-to-one communication in the here and now, it is even more effective when it permanently permeates the ward or institutional MILIEU. The term 'contact MILIEU' is usually applied to care settings where all staff (all professional staff, nursing staff, support staff and ancillary staff) are trained in using contact reflections in the service of better everyday care, a better social MILIEU in the institution, and more useful relationships with withdrawn people.

This method of working has been developed in a psychiatric ward setting by Dion Van Werde (Chapter 6 and Van Werde, 2002a) and in institutions caring for older people, or people with learning and other mental disabilities by Swiss psychologist, Marlis Pörtner (Chapter 8 and Pörtner, 2003/2007). When such an all-embracing *contact-MILIEU* is established, all aspects of care are made easier, more effective and more rewarding. We will look at how this is achieved in Chapter 6 and 7 with case studies of hospitals and care institutions where such regimes have been operating successfully for many years.

A contact MILIEU may be effective with the most challenging patients in situations where high levels of agitation, confusion and distress are debilitating for staff and contribute to a high-stress environment. And to reiterate the earlier point, it does not interfere with other psychological or medical interventions; indeed it has the potential to enhance them.

Contact work in general use in healthcare settings
'Contact work' is part of good, effective communication in care settings per se. It calls us to think how we *actually* engage with people and is new and unique in the sense that it gives this neglected issue the attention it deserves. Indeed, so neglected that it is the rule rather then the exception to identify 'treatment' with medication in many psychiatric settings, thus ignoring the importance of the quality of contact with patients for successful treatment. Contact work requires us to deliberately consider how to approach people who are in an altered state or 'pre-expressive' state (more of this on pages 25–7), which is why it has such potential for use in communication with people with a range of mental health and general health issues.

Contact work integrates the more formal aspects of Pre-Therapy such as 'contact reflections' into the general communication skills used to engage with a wide range of patients and service users. It teaches staff to be *explicit* about something that was, and is still perhaps, taken for granted. The new and different angle is that Garry Prouty gives the theoretical and philosophical foundations for how to engage with people who are not in psychological contact, or who are difficult for staff to engage with. He provides specific instructions on *what to look for* and *how to talk*. This is why his ideas have such instant resonance with nurses who get rather stuck on what to say to patients whether they are withdrawn due to a severe depressive state, withdrawn or difficult to understand in dementia, expressing ideas that are unusual (in PSYCHOSIS) to staff, or are less coherent due to a delirium or stroke.

If it is generally accepted 'evidence' that a wide range of professionals and carers in psychiatric services offer an empathic presence and develop a rapport with patients as part of their communication skills, then 'contact reflections' are simply part of this and Pre-Therapy helps further develop their ability to offer an empathic presence. In Pre-Therapy training this is done by being *explicit* and *very detailed* about the communication process with 'out-of-contact' patients using the contact reflections. This puts contact work in the same realm as listening, understanding and developing a support- and recovery-oriented relationship. Contact reflections can be seen as a way of using helpful communication skills, rather than a complete 'new therapy'.

It is unlikely that anyone in the healthcare professions would say: 'Where is the evidence base for listening to people?', 'We can't implement being empathic until the evidence base is there', or 'We won't do understanding until there is more evidence'. Contact reflections are the concrete minutiae of how we try to offer empathy, understanding and listening.

Notwithstanding Prouty's assertion that Pre-Therapy *is not a complete therapy*, we believe the evidence suggests that contact work is valuable and *generally therapeutic* in its own right for the following reasons:

1. It dissolves personal and social isolation and all of the secondary symptoms associated with such isolation.
2. It allows communication of everyday needs, thus facilitating more efficient and targeted everyday care, making patients generally more contact- and recovery-oriented.

3. It allows emotional expression to develop—an important precursor to therapeutic change in any approach that builds a
working alliance, and leads to more useful and *fulfilling*
communications for both patients and staff.

PRE-THERAPY UNDERPINNINGS

In Chapter 3 we will look in some detail at how Pre-Therapy is
done. So far we have implied that it is a method or set of techniques.
Whilst this is true, it is absolutely essential to realise that restoration
of contact should not be undertaken lightly or in a piecemeal
fashion (for more on this, see Chapters 7 and 9) without the
consequences having been planned for. A previously isolated
person restored to contact with themselves, the world and others,
will need different support and this will need careful thinking
through for each client group or individual.

Carers and staff not only need training in the 'instruments' of
Pre-Therapy, but should also have planned for the inevitable
changes to *their own* needs as their friends, relatives, clients or
patients respond to the contact work method.

It is only possible to make general statements of what to expect
when Pre-Therapy is used. Each setting and each person requires
some bespoke planning. However, we offer the following to help
readers at least make some sort of informed choice based on what
Pre-Therapy may or may not be able to achieve.

The practitioner

Anyone wanting to attempt Pre-Therapy or contact work should
realise that application of Pre-Therapy techniques cannot be done
in an acontextual, mechanical fashion. Not only is it an *essentially
human* activity, but certain responsibilities come with the territory.
The practitioner, in addition to using the techniques:

• Assumes full responsibility for contacting the client
• Validates the client's (e.g. PSYCHOTIC) experience
• Values the importance of the client's expressions
• Recognises that, e.g., hallucinations and DELUSIONS are
  meaningful

- Acknowledges the client's self-autonomy process towards meaningful experience
- Contributes to the client's healing process

Furthermore, an essential part of the context in which Pre-Therapy is enacted is the attitudinal set of the practitioner. The attitudes must be genuinely held and also evident in both the wider ethos and ambiance of the institution or personal and social environment of the client. These attitudes clearly point in a direction towards self-management, hope and recovery. They include:

- Compassion
- Acceptance
- Being non-critical
- Being non-judgemental
- Non-directiveness
- Interest and curiosity
- Receptivity to 'what is going on'
- Respect for clients' autonomy

Likely outcomes of Pre-Therapy

We will look later at research into Pre-Therapy and contact work, including its effectiveness. However, it's useful to summarise here the positive outcomes for clients, which can include one or more of the following:

- Reduction of (e.g. PSYCHOTIC) distress
- Clients become 'grounded' and more able to engage in daily life activities
- Fostering clients' trust with practitioner
- Emotional intelligence
- Clients are able to maintain feelings and COGNITIVE functioning —necessary to integrate painful experiences
- Clients develop a reality-based, informed choice regarding psychotherapy and other treatment input
- Clients become self-empowered and have the capacity to lead a life that fulfils their potential
- Better integration into society

Importantly, it is not only clients who benefit from Pre-Therapy or a contact MILIEU regime; there are also potential positive outcomes for staff which can include the following:

- Self-empowerment
- Increased awareness of different types of behavioural functioning
- Deeper understanding of levels of experiencing
- Satisfaction of developing skills to alleviate clients' hallucinations and DELUSIONS
- Ability to reduce clients' distress
- Increased ability to engage with clients
- Increased ability to earn the trust of clients
- Opportunity for greater involvement of the 'personhood' of staff member with the client
- Psychologists and psychiatrists have increased potential to understand the source of distress
- Opportunity for greater involvement of staff in a healing relationship
- An increase in job satisfaction
- Fewer re-admissions through the 'ever-revolving door'
- Possible financial and social benefits giving long-term cost reductions to care providers in some circumstances

Using Pre-Therapy interventions is not always plain sailing as we shall see in Penny Dodds' Chapter 9 (pp. 96–7). Anyone wishing to use Pre-Therapy methods must be tentative, respectful and ready to be guided by the needs of the person they are working with, when they become known. Sometimes, people who have been previously out of contact do not have a pleasant story to tell. Fear, anger, frustration and unusual experiences are made available by contact work, and it is rarely comfortable for the contact worker. Whilst therapists should be ready to engage with the difficult content and process which can surface when a person emerges from isolation, it is debatable whether nurses, carers and support workers can, or should be expected to, deal with such situations without careful preparation and additional training. It is with this warning that we move on to the next chapter.

3

UNDERSTANDING AND DOING
PRE-THERAPY AND CONTACT WORK

UNDERSTANDING PRE-THERAPY

Pre-Therapy as a method is deceptively simple. In practical terms it is a continual re-presentation of elements of shared reality, or as Prouty says, it 'points at the concrete'[1] offering and encouraging contact with self, the world and others. The elements of Pre-Therapy are:
  • Contact Functions (the client's process)
  • Contact Reflections (the therapist's responses)
  • Contact Behaviours (the client's behaviour)

Since this book is about *doing* Pre-Therapy and contact work, rather than the theory of psychological contact and Pre-Therapy, most chapters look at the helper-therapist end of Pre-Therapy (contact reflections), rather than the client end (contact behaviours). We begin, however, with a very short introduction to the terminology and ideas of the whole theory. Readers wanting to understand *how* and *why* clients might be out of contact will need to look at some fairly specialised books, chapters and papers in narrower fields such as theories of PSYCHOSIS, DISSOCIATION, brain damage and neuropsychology.

Contact Functions
As we have seen, when we say a person is in psychological contact, we have to ask 'what is in contact with what?' Specifically, in Pre-Therapy theory, the FULLY FUNCTIONING person is able to be in contact with the world, their own feelings and other people.
  • *Reality Contact.* Awareness of the 'world', specifically people, places, things and events
  • *Affective Contact.* Awareness of one's own moods, feelings and emotions

---
1. Garry Prouty borrows the phrase from philosopher Martin Buber (1964: 547).

- *Communicative Contact.* The SYMBOLISATION of the world (reality) and self to others—using words or sentences

An individual may lose one or all of these contact functions for any of the reasons covered in Chapter 2, pages 17 and 18. It is essential to work bearing in mind the understanding that every person loses contact in a unique way. Restoration of the contact functions is the goal of Pre-Therapy and it is important to reiterate that although it may be simple to state as a goal, it is, more often than not, difficult to achieve. Furthermore, Pre-Therapy techniques appear deceptively simple, indeed, many carers, support workers and experienced helping professionals may confidently assert that they 'are doing it already'. However, after seeing an experienced Pre-Therapy practitioner, the differences between occasional ad hoc attempts to make contact, and planned, mindful Pre-Therapy sessions or institutional contact MILIEU, become strikingly apparent. Without intending to diminish the skill and effort put in by helpers to restoring psychological contact with those in their care, it is unlikely that they have been attempting interventions for long enough or with sufficient pervasive persistence and attention to detail.

Expressive functioning
When all contact functions are engaged and fully working, in Pre-Therapy terms this is called 'expressive functioning'. It is called *expressive* because the person is in touch with themselves, the world and others and can not only experience this, but also express or communicate their experience. It is the psychological state of being that most of us enjoy most of the time, take for granted (because it is not usually the 'figure' in our field of attention, it is the 'ground', the water in which we swim), and is required in order that counselling and psychotherapy, and indeed everyday functioning, can take place.

Pre-expressive functioning
When an individual is experiencing some degree of contact-impairment, we might not easily be able to tell whether on the one hand the person *has the capacity for contact* but is *unable to make contact.* Or on the other hand, the person might be

deliberately and consciously withdrawing from contact, although she is able to be in contact if she chooses, yet does not wish to be in psychological contact. A person in the former state, *capable* but *unable,* is, according to Prouty, 'pre-expressive'. They are a person 'locked inside' an uncommunicative shell, i.e. they have a 'pre-expressive self' imprisoned, unable to communicate.

An early experience with his brother who suffered severe and enduring learning disability informed Prouty's later theory:

> One day, when I was eleven or twelve years old, I invited a friend to visit my home. We were talking when I said 'I wonder if he [brother] understands what we are saying?' To my intense surprise, he responded, 'You know I do, Garry' and then lapsed back into a regressed and autistic state. For years the experience haunted me, giving me a feeling there was 'somebody in there'. (Prouty, 1998: 82)

Prouty discovered that this experience of there being 'somebody in there' was not unique. Psychiatrist Luc Roelens offers a similar story in a clinical setting:

> A sixty-year-old chronic SCHIZOPHRENIC had slipped into a dementia-like state. For weeks he was unable to speak, he had to be fed by the nurses and had lost control of his sphincter. One day, a nurse offered him a Coke. He choked, coughed, and in doing so, emitted a cloud of droplets of Coke that hit her face. Visibly startled he immediately and clearly said 'Excuse me, I did not intend to do that'. Before the nurse was able to answer him he had sunk again into a dementia-like state … (Roelens, 1994: xii)

Such recoveries are not always fleeting. Roelens cites Stromgren (1991) who presents a case study concerning a farmer's wife:

> She immediately recovered from a chronic and severe CATATONIC state upon receiving the message that her husband had fallen down from a roof and broken both legs. Her intention 'to go home to take care of everything there' was strong enough to dispel the thought disorders and defective behaviours. Occasional follow-ups after four and ten years revealed that she functioned as an efficient housewife … (Stromgren 1991: 30–40, cited in Roelens, 1994: xii)

These incidents are examples of serendipitous, unexpected, atheoretical restoration of expressive functioning. Pre-Therapy, however, is a *systematic method* aiming to achieve the restoration of expressive functioning, with the permission of the client/patient.

The concept of pre-expressive functioning also embraces the kinds of verbal behaviours that signal the person's hitherto unintelligible struggle to make contact. Prouty calls these 'pre-expressive signs'. In Prouty's words, such signs are 'pre-symbolic thrust[s] toward reality' (Prouty, 1998: 83). An important feature of pre-expressive signs (however immediately nonsensical they sound) is that they frequently *do have meaning*, if only the helper can understand. However, understanding the meaning of pre-expressive utterances requires time, care, high-quality attention and humility. The meaning is often oblique and embedded in the client's story which has yet to be told.

So we should approach out-of-contact, pre-expressive people with the tentative expectation that they can become expressive and that they are trying to make contact through what to us appears to be nonsensical speech. We should seek meaning in their utterances, as a possibly distorted window into a hidden reality. Pre-Therapy, as we shall see in this chapter, tries to access this reality by using 'primitive', 'concrete', irreducibly basic reflections.

Grey-zone functioning

The difference between pre-expressive and expressive functioning is not always clear. Dion Van Werde (Van Werde, 2002a) introduced the term 'grey-zone' to indicate this region where people oscillate sometimes almost imperceptibly between pre-expressive and expressive functioning. Figures 1 and 2 overleaf illustrate this.

In the grey-zone, a person's contact functions are variable, moving in and out of contact in a few minutes or seconds. Depending upon the person, the out-of-contact state can vary from mild DISSOCIATION to a fleeting FLORID hallucination or DELUSION. It is in the grey-zone that the helper or therapist must be on full alert, looking for pre-expressive signs and distinguishing between them and full-contact, congruent, expressive communication. Here the helper or therapist shifts from primarily listening to looking.

Figure 1: Client's level of functioning (from Van Werde, 2002a)

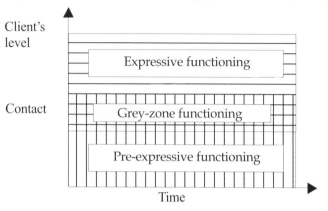

Figure 2: Client's grey-zone functioning (from Van Werde, 2002a)

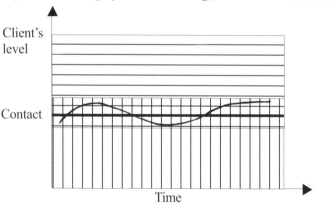

And as we discovered in the previous chapter, using Pre-Therapy methods requires a sympathetic and supportive environment. We will see examples of working in the grey-zone in Chapters 5 and 6.

Contact behaviours

The client's behaviour is the window to their world and we rely on their behaviour to help us understand what is going on for them. The problem with a contact-impaired person is that these behaviours are both minimal in comparison with normal everyday social communications, and often idiosyncratic and difficult to decipher.

In Pre-Therapy terms, behaviours which give some indication of the expressiveness of a person, or how well they are able to make contact, are called *contact behaviours*. In a clinical setting improvement in contact can be measured by increased contact behaviour.

At one level it would be true to say that *every* behaviour is potentially contact behaviour, and it is important that we approach every client in every setting with this firmly in mind. The helper has to have their antennae up and sensitivity set to 'high' to pick up expressive signs and contact behaviours. Helpers should be particularly interested when the client:

- talks about events, places, things and people (indicating reality contact)
  'The light is in my eyes.' 'The chair is comfortable.' 'When will the car be here?' 'I am going home this afternoon.'
- talks about or makes facial expressions or bodily postures of emotional or feeling content (indicating affective contact)
  Kicking the chair; grimacing in sadness; smiling; using feeling words such as 'happy', 'angry', 'upset', etc.
- uses words indicating social awareness (indicating communicative contact)
  'Can I talk to you?' 'I don't like it when you shout at me.' 'I need my father here.'

The helper using Pre-Therapy methods must pay close attention to expressions, posture, words and non-language utterances in order to 'stay with' the client. At any one time they will have to make decisions about whether, on the one hand, the client is out of contact and making a pre-expressive communication, and, given what the helper already knows about the client, whether this has any meaning. On the other hand, the client might be making emergent expressive contact, and the helper would interpret this as restoration of one or more contact functions.

Attempts to measure contact behaviour based on Pre-Therapy

theory began with Hinterkopf, Prouty and Brunswick (1979) and the Pre-Therapy Rating Scale (PTRS), which was later revised by Garry Prouty. Aldo Dinacci (1997) developed the Evaluation Criterion for the Pre-Therapy Interview (ECPI) scale and these are reviewed by Dekeyser, Prouty and Elliott (in press). These scales will be very briefly explained in Chapter 10, p. 107.

DOING PRE-THERAPY

If you have turned straight to this section without first reading Chapter 2 and the first part of this chapter, I suggest that you prepare yourself by going back and looking at this preliminary material. Without any apology whatsoever, I recommend this to avoid the shock of seeing how simple the techniques of Pre-Therapy are, at least in the reading of the descriptions. You will also then have read my repeated reiteration of the fact that Pre-Therapy, whilst easy to describe, is actually difficult to do. We shall learn more about these difficulties throughout this book. It is likely to be difficult for the following reasons:

- it is a special sort of communication for special circumstances
- it can be embarrassing or awkward to use contact reflections at first
- it requires time and patience, since it can sometimes take a long time to produce noticeable results
- people already qualified as helpers (psychotherapists, psychologists, counsellors, nurses, etc.) will almost certainly have problems in scaling down their responses to the minimalist, concrete responses necessary for successful contact work
- some of the time spent doing contact work can be in silence, or at a slow tempo to match the lived experience of the client which may add to the awkwardness for people unused to silent or slow-paced attention-giving (although paradoxically, sometimes the client's behaviour can be extremely rapid)
- when helpers get involved in the process with their client or friend, they can forget to keep it very simple and absolutely basic in the heat of the moment

The practice of Pre-Therapy is making what are called *contact reflections*. These are the building-blocks of empathic contact, used in a unilateral effort by the helper to make psychological contact. They are concrete, duplicative and repetitive. In other words they are plain, meticulously literal reflections which respectfully duplicate, mimic and repeat the client's behaviour and utterances. They repeatedly re-present the commonplace reality of the environment and are 'sensitive to the concrete particularity' (Prouty, Van Werde & Pörtner, 2002: 16) of the client's behaviour.

Contact Reflections
There are five types of contact reflection, and in Pre-Therapy transcripts and texts the abbreviations are in standard use.
- *Situational Reflections* (SR) Reflecting aspects of the shared environment (people, places, events and things)
- *Facial Reflections* (FR) Reflecting verbally or by 'mimicking' the facial expressions of the client
- *Body Reflections* (BR) Reflecting, verbally or posturally, the gestures, movement and postures of the client
- *Word-for-Word Reflections* (WWR) Repeating back what the client says word for word
- *Reiterative Reflections* (RR) Remaking contact by repetition of previous reflections that showed an effect

Vignette 1
To illustrate how the various types of contact reflections can be used in isolation and in combination, the following fictional vignette is presented. Readers should note that the pauses and other events are just as important as the verbal responses.

The action takes place in a nursing home between Mary, an 87-year-old woman who is suffering from dementia, and Lucy, her granddaughter. Mary only speaks occasionally, usually muttering a few words under her breath which can only be heard with considerable effort, and even then seem to make no sense to the passing carer. Lucy has learned Pre-Therapy contact reflections as part of her training as a mental health nurse and has set some time aside to visit her grandmother. The nursing home staff make sure that Mary is in her private room when Lucy comes to visit.

Lucy 1: Hello Grandma, [*kisses her on the forehead*], it's Lucy, your granddaughter. How are you?

[*Mary, who was staring into space out of the window, turns her eyes in Lucy's direction, but not far enough to see her. Lucy walks into Mary's line of vision …*]

Mary 1: … 2 minutes silence …

Lucy 2: We're in your room at Hesford Grange. You were looking out of the window and tried look at me but couldn't go far enough. I've walked round to see you properly. (SR)

Mary 2: … 30 second silence … [*she looks down, then fleetingly at Lucy, then out of the window*].

… 30 second pause …

Lucy 3: Grandma looked down, then looked at Lucy and is now looking out of the window. (SR)

Mary 3: … 1 minute silence … sigh … [*whilst continuing to look glazed out of the window*]

Lucy 4: Grandma sighs [*Lucy makes a sighing sound* (WWR)] and looks out of the window. (RR, SR)

Mary 4: … 2 minutes silence … [*continuing to look glazedly out of the window*]

Lucy 5: You're sitting in your chair looking out of the window (RR) of your room. The sun is shining outside. (SR)

Mary 5: … 2 minutes silence … mnnnnnnnnn [*pause*] go … go.

Lucy 6: You say 'mmnnnnn, go, go'. (WWR)

Mary 6: Go.

Lucy 7: Go (WWR)

Mary 7: [*looks at Lucy*] Go.

Lucy 8: You look at Lucy (SR) and say 'go'. (WWR)

Mary 8: Yes.

Lucy 9: Yes (WWR)

Mary 9: … 1 minute silence … [*moves her hand from her lap to the arm of the chair*] Yes.

Lucy 10: You moved your hand like this [*makes the same*

movement] (BR) and say 'yes'. (WWR)

Mary 10: … silence … [*Silence for 4 minutes*]

Lucy 11: You are sitting in your room with Lucy, you look out of the window. (SR) You say 'go, go, yes'. (RR, WWR) Do you want Lucy to go so that you can sit alone?

Mary 11: Mmnnnnnn, no! [*She frowns and grimaces, looking frustrated.*]

Lucy 12: Mmnnnnnn, no! (WWR) You screw up your face, frustrated. (FR)

…30 second silence …

Mary 12: No! Yes, side. [*Mary turns her head and looks at Lucy directly and frowns.*]

Lucy 13: No! Yes, side. (WWR) You frown and look at Lucy (SR) and say 'No! Yes, side' (RR) Do you want to lie down on your side?

Mary 13: No!! Yes … go … out … side.

[*Lucy then asks the staff if they can arrange for a wheelchair to take her Grandma outside.*]

This is a simple and fairly straightforward example of using Pre-Therapy contact reflections. It tries to give an impression of the slow pace required by the setting, the repetitive and concrete nature of the reflections, and the silences. The whole exchange takes around 20 minutes. There is no such thing as a 'typical' duration of a contact work or Pre-Therapy session. Contact work tends to be ad hoc, on the fly, led by demand or the situation (although there is no absolute reason why a 'session' could not be planned). Pre-Therapy tends to be planned and conducted by professional helpers as the necessary preliminary to therapy. Depending upon the situation and the client, contact work can be a few seconds interaction through to a permanent 24-hour-a-day MILIEU. A Pre-Therapy 'session' can be a few minutes to several hours in one go, or a planned, fixed duration each day or week.

In the above vignette we clearly see how the contact-impaired person moves from pre-expressive functioning to expressive functioning. (It is intended to be a simple example with no intention of illustrating variable grey-zone functioning.) On a couple of occasions Lucy thinks that she has spotted enough pre-expressive signs and contact behaviours to check that she has understood her grandma correctly and that her grandma is in contact. These are:

- When Mary looks at Lucy and says 'go' and 'yes' in (Mary) M7 & M8. Lucy's way of checking is a question 'Do you want Lucy to go so that you can sit alone?' in (Lucy) L11.
- When Mary looks at Lucy in M12, and when she says 'No! Yes, side' in M13. Again Lucy's way of checking is a question 'Do you want to lie down on your side?' in L13.
- When Lucy is sure she understands she accommodates her Grandma's wishes by arranging for her to go outside.

Vignette 2

A psychotherapist working in a psychiatric hospital has a first appointment with a voluntary in-patient. Dameer is a newly qualified therapist and Zafar is six days into his first hospital admission after being diagnosed with a first episode of 'schizophrenia'. Zafar asked to see a male therapist and Dameer was available.

Zafar 1: [*Comes in the room and sits down with precision and a sense of urgency, he looks intently at Dameer as though he recognises him, looking straight into his eyes.*]

Dameer 1: Hi Zafar, I'm Dameer. You asked on the ward to see someone. We've got about three-quarters of an hour and I'm ready to listen to whatever you want to talk about.

Zafar 2: [*Continues to look intently, just short of staring, into Dameer's eyes, as though waiting for something to happen.*]

Dameer 2: [*Isn't sure whether Zafar is out of contact, but decides to use contact reflections anyway*.] You are sitting, looking intently into my eyes. We are in a room in Oldfield Hospital. (SR, BR)

Zafar 3: [*Still silent, Zafar turns briefly to glance at the door, as though checking that it's closed.*]

Dameer 3: You quickly looked at the door then back at me. (BR) [*Dameer points to his own eyes and makes a slightly*

> *exaggerated movement with them towards the door and back,*
> *whilst talking.*] (BR)

Zafar 4: [*Still looking intently at Dameer.*] I have to check you out.

Dameer 4: You look at me and say 'I have to check you out'.
(BR, WWR)

Zafar 5: [*Silence for 2 minutes, still looking at Dameer*]

Dameer 5: You have to check me out. (RR)

Zafar 6: I thought it was time we talked about the messages.

Dameer 6: You want to talk about some messages. [*Dameer*
treats this as a response to congruent communication, i.e. he
thinks they are in contact and responds with an empathic
reflection.]

Zafar 7: The messages all around here. In and out, everywhere
in the air. [*He makes a weaving motion with his hands.*]

Dameer 7: The messages all around here. In and out everywhere
in the air. (WWR) [*Dameer copies the weaving motion with*
his hands.] (BR)

Zafar 8: Yes, the messages are everywhere. Can't you see them,
down the corridors? [*He looks and sounds surprised.*]

Dameer 8: You look surprised. (FR) You say you see messages
everywhere down the corridors and ask me if I can see them
too. (SR)

[*The session continues like this for around twenty minutes during*
which time Zafar looks increasingly thoughtful and less
distracted. He says that people talk about him in the hospital
and at home and send messages through the air to each other
about him. Zafar then says that he would like to go and gets up
and abruptly walks out.]

The session shows how to respond to pre-expressive words and
sentences which have meaning for the client but may not be
understandable in the here and now to the therapist. Because
Dameer isn't coming in to the session with any preconceived ideas
about Zafar's level of functioning, he has to make the generalised
assumption to be ready for anything and flexible in his responses.

In (Dameer) D2 he isn't sure what Zafar's responses might
mean, so he 'plays safe' and decides to use contact reflections.

This is a safe option because the worst that can happen is that Zafar might be a little puzzled by the concreteness of the response. Dameer quickly understands that Zafar is out of contact as a result of his response.

In D6, he thinks he understands Zafar and responds as such. However, Zafar's next response tells him that Zafar is still out of reach and that he (Dameer) understands nothing. Dameer might *guess* what meaning Zafar's words might have, but from here on he largely sticks to contact reflections rather than making interpretations.

Other examples

More extracts and vignettes are given in subsequent chapters to illustrate particular issues in particular settings. What cannot be conveyed in these brief vignettes is the pace and timing of the reflections. There can be two extremes of this process:

- in some of Prouty's case studies and transcripts, the sessions last for many hours with very long periods of silence, the therapist continually vigilant
- in other cases, the practitioner must reflect at a very high speed e.g., where a client is hypomanic, the practitioner will have to take advantage of very brief pauses between breaths if they are to have any chance of being perceived by the client and 'earn a place' in their world
- practitioners also need to be ready to shift modes from auditory to visual or bodily/facial reflections in order to reach through the client's symptomatology and be noticed, rather than just be a part of the 'wallpaper' of the client's world

In many contexts Pre-Therapy and contact work are very demanding of the helpers. In the next chapter we look at contact work and Pre-Therapy from a carer's point of view, where the requirement is to be sensitively judging the status of every communication and ready to respectfully respond to the other person, twenty-four hours a day.

4

A CARER'S EXPERIENCE[1] OF
PRE-THERAPY AND CONTACT WORK

Background to our nightmare

My experience of the mental health system started in the mid 80s, when I was concerned that my son was dyslexic and I requested a consultation with a specialist. The specialist informed me that he wasn't dyslexic—despite my son receiving no tests—and I was told that I was worrying unnecessarily which neither helped my son nor alleviated my growing concerns. He had few friends and began to struggle with getting up to go to school. When I was at my wits' end to know how to help him, I requested an appointment with a psychiatrist.

My son and I were seen separately. He was acutely distressed after each appointment and soon refused to see the psychiatrist. Despite his distress he obtained nine GCSEs (general education exams at age 16 in England) at top grades, but on the first day of his A-level (advanced level exams at age 18 in England) exams, he told me that he had absconded and spent the day cycling in the country. He was admitted to an adolescent unit, diagnosed with depression and anxiety, prescribed various antidepressants and referred to a psychiatrist in another health authority who arranged a place at an anxiety management group.

After a couple of short-term jobs and much family encouragement he was employed as a trainee butcher, with the full assurance of being trained as a butcher, but was dismissed on Christmas Eve, six weeks after commencing because another butcher had returned to work from sick leave. Feeling deceived, his depression returned. As his depression deepened he was prescribed Prozac. As the Prozac dose was increased, he began

---

1. Catherine Clarke's experience is her and her son's personal experience of the UK psychiatric system. Provision of services and the attitudes of staff may be different in other regions and countries.

to experience vivid nightmares and acted on them is if they were reality-based—prompted on one occasion to give a large sum of money to charity. I later learned that both nightmares and PSYCHOTIC experiencing are amongst the adverse effects of PROZAC—his first acute PSYCHOTIC crisis soon followed.

After distressing nights lying awake listening to my son having verbal conversations about religion in his bedroom, hearing him shriek and scream in terror and fearing that the situation had the potential of becoming violent, we called 999 and soon the police and a crisis team arrived. After SECTIONING him, the Responsible Medical Officer (RMO) diagnosed SCHIZOPHRENIA, discontinued PROZAC abruptly and began treatment with an atypical NEUROLEPTIC. The pharmacologist stated that he would have to take medication for at least twelve months. We weren't informed about adverse effects—we learnt about these as the NEUROLEPTICS took a hold over my son.

IN THE GRIP OF THE MENTAL HEALTH SYSTEM

I began my own research into SCHIZOPHRENIA and NEUROLEPTIC treatment. The research I discovered contained information which professionals had failed to disclose to either my son or myself. On reading how the NEUROLEPTICS were impacting on my son's central nervous system, I felt a deep sense of revulsion. My trust in the mental health system plummeted to rock bottom.

My son's many crises appeared to fit in with the academic literature about SUPER SENSITIVITY PSYCHOSIS (SSP). I realised that my son's extreme sensitivity to medication resulted in him being chronically over-medicated and the NEUROLEPTICS were actually inducing and perpetuating his PSYCHOSIS. The prevailing psychiatric belief—that NEUROLEPTICS are *anti*PSYCHOTICS—appeared not to be the case for my son.

When I took the research for my son's Multi-Disciplinary Team (MDT) members to read, professional people would not give their opinion on it, despite it appearing extremely relevant to their NEUROLEPTIC treatment of my son. Invariably his SSP crisis resulted in the RMO attributing it to a 'relapse'—a worsening of his illness and further evidence of SCHIZOPHRENIA. His medication was either increased or changed to a different NEUROLEPTIC. It all seemed so random, rather like NEUROLEPTIC roulette.

When my son realised the NEUROLEPTICS were having a negative effect on his quality of life, he tried to withdraw from NEUROLEPTICS. My husband and I supported him. Due to our ignorance of NEUROLEPTIC withdrawal, he experienced a PSYCHOTIC EPISODE. The RMO regarded this PSYCHOSIS as still further proof that my son needed to be medicated—giving the psychiatrist additional weight to his prescribing even more NEUROLEPTIC treatment. I realised that this PSYCHOSIS was connected with withdrawal and this corresponded with my research into TARDIVE PSYCHOSIS. My son had basically gone 'cold turkey'.

On another occasion when the RMO withdrew my son's Lorazepam too abruptly, he began to experience PSYCHOTIC symptoms within twelve hours. On a different occasion, six weeks after being admitted into a closed unit my son began to despair that he would ever see his home again. He became acutely distressed and experienced greater trauma through hallucinations. The MDT attributed my son's PSYCHOSIS to his SCHIZOPHRENIC illness, to the exclusion of any other possible rationale.

A further symptom was my son's lack of personal hygiene. I queried whether any MDT member had taken an interest in asking what difficulty my son was experiencing with his hygiene. On asking my son, I discovered he was reluctant to bath because the towels did not dry effectively and there was no change of clean clothing. These are all valid APSYCHOTIC reasons for not bathing and at that particular time had nothing at all to do with PSYCHOTIC symptomatology.

On most occasions when I spoke to the RMO and Care Trust Managers about SCHIZOPHRENIA and NEUROLEPTIC treatment, I was looked at with incredulity, as though I had no right to comment. This was confirmed when I was told by the Mental Health Commission psychiatrist in no uncertain terms to leave such matters to them, the professionals. I got the message loud and clear. As a carer, they regarded the treatment of my son as none of my business. I disagree—this *is* my business when I see what my son has been made to suffer.

Within a few days of starting medication with a particular NEUROLEPTIC, he began to suffer Parkinsonian-induced shaking and the standard anti-CHOLINERGIC drug only gave him minimal relief. AKATHESIA, yet another adverse effect, made my son pace up and down the corridor continuously. When he was at home he walked round and round the house and up and down the garden. Trying to settle down to watch television or read was an impossibility. His only relief was when he was asleep. This inner restlessness became so intolerable that my son said he would rather commit suicide than to suffer in this way for the rest of his life.

After one year my son began to develop involuntary facial movements. These included the blowing out of his cheeks, puffing through his lips and the protrusion of his tongue—his mouth looked full of tongue and eating became difficult. I recognised these as symptoms of TARDIVE DYSKINESIA (TD). I had been dreading this, as I knew from my research that TD is potentially irreversible. Many older people develop these facial movements— it is a part of the aging process and results from the degeneration of the nerve endings in the brain. I was so concerned that I requested a referral to a neurologist for my son to be assessed. The RMO delayed this request indefinitely. A new RMO in the ward round placed emphasis on how 'the benefits outweigh the risks' regarding medication—as if acknowledging my son had TD but that this was acceptable because of the benefits of the drugs. We then received a letter from him which declared that in his opinion my son was not suffering from TD. This seemed to be an attempt to absolve himself from taking responsibility for the damage to my son's brain, brought about by his treatment.

Eventually two private neurologists diagnosed my son's TD and recommended that the NEUROLEPTIC drugs be discontinued, in accordance with pharmaceutical literature surrounding TD. Despite this, at a later date an NHS neurologist claimed that he did not know the reason for my son's facial movements. This NHS non-diagnosis was upheld for three years before one NHS psychiatrist finally acknowledged the diagnosis of TD.

Coercive behaviour on the part of mental health professionals has been commonplace. A social worker, who I had entrusted to see my son alone in our home, told my son that he would extend his SECTION for another year if he did not comply with attending group therapy. My son was left crying uncontrollably. One RMO stated that since my son had difficulty in expressing himself—she thought it appropriate that he should be SECTIONED and yet another RMO stated that he would extend the SECTION until my son spoke about his problems. As a caring and responsible parent, I feel incensed when my vulnerable son is threatened and I am sure that threatening behaviour is not conducive to a trusting relationship.

In a closed unit, my son felt professionally badgered for six months, due to the pressure from the Multi-Disciplinary Team (MDT) who wanted his agreement to increase medication. Browbeaten, he eventually succumbed in a Care Programme meeting. His statement was duly recorded and acted upon immediately by the RMO. In private my son told me his reason for finally agreeing —he just wanted to get them off his back. He also thought that if he was obedient and complied with their need to increase medication, he would be allowed to return home. This did not occur for many months since there were indications that the unit guidelines directed staff towards keeping my son locked up for a year, followed by another year locked up on a closed rehabilitation unit.

As a routine, my son was *told* what NEUROLEPTIC to take and was *told* that if he stopped taking the medication he would become ill. This emphasis on medication was further coercion intended to frighten him into submitting to treatment he did not want. Sometimes though, staff bypassed any discussions, coercive or otherwise about treatment and instead simply used their ability to SECTION him.

Many of the signs and symptoms that my son experienced in that terrible time are described by NEUROLEPTIC MALIGNANT SYNDROME, a potentially life-threatening situation. It transpired that before the ACUPHASE treatment was started, half of the MDT had wanted this SECTION applied because it provided legal protection in the case of my son's death. Another RMO in a

SECTIONING situation did declare that he was endangering my son's physical life but he would take full clinical responsibility.

My son was getting worse, not better. He was receiving all sorts of different medication treatments, but *only* medication. He had not received any psychological help at all. I was told that psychological treatment was not included as part of treatment on the acute ward. My husband and I worked hard to persuade one RMO along these lines by influencing the Trust managers to allow a special provision for 'talking treatment' for my son. Part of this 'talking treatment' necessitated my son writing down his hallucinations and DELUSIONS, together with the potential triggering factor with the date and time. Although he attempted to write a few of his experiences, this exercise posed him some difficulties. His concentration was impeded due to the sedation effect of medication at that point in time. Another side effect impaired his COGNITIVE functioning making it harder for him to work things out. It transpired that the psychologist's input was primarily designed to correct my son's behaviour in order to ease the nurses' management of my son. When he was acutely PSYCHOTIC on a closed unit, a PSI (PSYCHOSOCIAL INTERVENTION) psychologist stated he was too PSYCHOTIC for therapy. Neither psychologist made progress and both gave up, my son being classified as unsuitable for therapy.

PRE-THERAPY

My distress at seeing my son constantly PSYCHOTIC propelled me to pluck up the courage to try to link with him by trying Garry Prouty's Pre-Therapy contact method. I felt greatly encouraged when I found that I was able to decrease his distress by grounding him back into our shared reality. As I developed an interest in this approach, I also became more aware that some of his body language and fragmented words were connected with situations from his past. I realised that his hallucinations had some meaning for him. This seemed to be an alien concept to professionals who saw his PSYCHOTIC expressions as unimportant and needing to be stamped out or suppressed at all costs; no one considered his PSYCHOTIC experiencing to have any potential value in helping my son in the long term.

On discovering I was able to help my son, I made contact with Garry Prouty, who invited me to a Pre-Therapy International Network meeting and I eventually attended workshops run by Garry Prouty and Dion Van Werde. I realised Pre-Therapy provided me with the vital link, essential for all professionals, to be able connect with people experiencing PSYCHOSIS—enabling them to have meaningful conversations. I began to share this knowledge with various Care Trust personnel. COGNITIVE BEHAVIOURAL THERAPY and PSI psychologists were uninterested, preferring to focus on their particular approach. One nurse seemed to find my knowledge threatening and became defensive, claiming she had nursed and managed patients for over twenty years. Only one nurse who was present when I was working with my son realised that I was able to make contact with him.

Using contact reflections as a carer
After talking to and learning from Garry Prouty and members of the Pre-Therapy International Network, I was encouraged to try using contact reflections with my son. I understood that the reflections draw attention to the immediate surroundings and expressions, verbal and non-verbal, of the other person with no guessing, interpreting or jumping to conclusions. I had to work with only what I could clearly see and hear. This can be difficult when you have a strong existing relationship with the other person as a friend, relative and/or carer. For a carer, contact work is just as much about what you *don't* do as what you *do* do.

Some examples of the different types of contact reflections used with my son are as follows:

Situational Reflections
One evening, at home, my son experienced a FLORID episode and began shrieking in terror. I said: 'You are at home, it's ten o'clock in the evening, you are in the sitting room, the cat is on the chair, Daddy is sitting with you.' Within a short space of time, he became less distracted and was able to interact more helpfully with people around him.

Facial Reflections

Whenever my son looked sad I would simply say 'You look sad', in a warm but straightforward manner. Such plain, direct, reflections seemed to help him get in touch with his feelings of, on those occasions, sadness. He was also enabled to *express* his previously concealed feelings of sadness. Uncomplicated facial reflections helped him express a wide range of emotions, not only sadness.

Body Reflections

On one occasion when my son was mute, he slowly lifted his arm towards his chest. I said 'Your arm is pointing to your chest' and lifted my arm to my chest in a similar movement. This helped him find the first few faltering words which soon led to an animated conversation.

Word-for-Word Reflections

This type of reflection often comes quite naturally to carers in private moments with the people they care for. When my son had regressed to a child-like state, he repeatedly said 'monkey'. In turn I repeated 'monkey' and he gradually introduced other single words, such as 'magic' and 'tricked' which ultimately led to him talking about feeling deceived.

Reiterative Reflections

Based on previous reflections which initiated a response, these also come quite naturally to many carers. In the situation described above when my son was regressed, I noticed that he was staring ahead intently. After reflecting the word 'monkey' several times, I saw him turn his head to look at me. My next response was: 'When I said "monkey" you looked at me'. This indicated to him that there had been a reaction which I had noticed; some communication offered and received, some give and take, the beginning of contact.

As I used contact reflections more and more, my son began to sense that I was able to help in a way that, for example, 'nursing as usual' did not. One day he telephoned me to ask me to visit him urgently in hospital to 'ground' him because 'the nurses don't know what to do'.

It isn't possible for me to do justice to the finer points of contact work, since everything revolves around the uniqueness of each person and each moment, but, as a carer I have made some discoveries which others might find useful:
- Paying attention closely to the smallest behaviours is vital
- Sometimes a person's contact level can be lowered by overly repetitious reflection or if the pace of reflections is too slow
- Conversely, if reflections are given too quickly or profusely, the person may get overwhelmed. Distress can be reduced by slowing the pace of reflections
- People in acute psychotic states can react strongly to the physical closeness of others; give plenty of space. Distance frequently helps alleviate distress

THE RESPONSE OF THE TRADITIONAL MENTAL HEALTH SERVICES

Minimal interest was shown by professionals in the success I was achieving with my son, so I went further afield to get support and made contact with universities and Care Trusts. A Reader in Mental Health at a Midlands university recognised the importance of Prouty's work and supported me in giving several Pre-Therapy taster workshops. Many people showed interest and I received positive feedback on several occasions although following one presentation, the presiding nursing tutor told her students that if they used this skill they would be struck off from the course.

In this inner world of the mental health system, I experienced professionals acting like gods, who reign supreme with their 'received medical wisdom'. I experienced professionals' rigid compliance with treatment in relation to national and local policies. I have felt powerless to help my son in SECTIONING situations and vulnerable in the face of their power and control of my son.

My ultimate frustration and exasperation occurred when, on a closed unit, the MDT members made a united stance in refusing to help my son with Prouty's contact work. Seeing my son being needlessly distressed at the expense of this collective decision, I began to confront their psychiatric practice together with professional attitudes and behaviour. The MDT reacted defensively by involving the Trust managers, who summoned me and my husband to a meeting. Their issues included, disproportionate amount of time spent dealing with us as relatives; attitudes, behaviour and manner directed at staff; and difficulties arising from differences of opinion regarding treatment and its consequences. Initially I felt threatened. Then I realised that I was receiving all the blame for these issues. There was no indication of professionals' accountability for their behaviour in our relationship. It was as though all their behaviour was impeccable and unquestionable. I certainly didn't feel understood in my distress.

At the height of my son's great emotional distress, *he* always had to understand what the nurses wanted from him. For their part, the nurses made little or no attempt to understand the reason for his anger or what it was like to be in his shoes. Not being understood only served to heighten his distress.

On one occasion when he was refused home leave, the nurse abruptly left him without seeing what effect this terrible news would have on him. My son reacted (typically for him, when he felt misunderstood and isolated) by lashing out. He was pounced upon, manhandled and frogmarched down to the isolation room. When the door opened for him to be given extra sedation I could hear him shrieking in anger and indignation. I offered to sit with him. Sitting beside him, he began to sob profusely. We returned to his room, where he verbally expressed his feelings about the nurses. I reflected what I thought was going on for him. 'You're angry and all you want to do is to hurt the nurses.' He nodded. 'You want to come home. I want you to come home. I am not sure how we are going to manage this, but we will work on this together.' He felt understood and became calmer.

A DOUBLE-EDGED DISCOVERY

After a GENOTYPING test, it was discovered that my son had inefficient functioning of CYTOCHROME P-450 2D6. The CYP 2D6 is an important CYTOCHROME for metabolising and excreting NEUROLEPTIC drugs. Consequently his body has accumulated excessive amounts of these drugs and has resulted in him experiencing severe adverse reactions together with repeated SUPER SENSITIVITY PSYCHOSIS. So although I used contact reflections with him with some effect, Pre-Therapy progress was limited by this NEUROLEPTIC-genetic combination. My son's genetic inability to metabolise PSYCHOTROPIC drugs, together with inevitable 'SECTIONS' with enforced NEUROLEPTIC treatment, cyclic readmissions, long stays on wards and units, and his experiences of feeling misunderstood and unheard, have all increased his despair, distrust and fear of being treated within the mental health system.

These are factors that have contributed to my son's lack of recovery. Pre-Therapy can only go so far and I think it is unrealistic to expect contact reflections in an informal carer relationship to overcome the terrible weight of all of these factors, particularly the brick wall of his defunct enzymes.

Within these limitations, it is obvious to me that the key to psychological healing lies within the relationship between the clinician and client. I think my son would undoubtedly benefit from a therapeutic healing relationship with clinicians and nurses who embrace the values of contact work, Pre-Therapy and the person-centred approach: these optimal conditions promote psychotherapeutic growth.

Pre-Therapy is an approach that does not deny, collude or smother PSYCHOTIC distress. It enables clinicians and nurses to know 'what to say' and 'how to be' with clients: it has the potential to bring more safety and satisfaction and more humanity to the mental health environment. Pre-Therapy is an open door, an opportunity for clinicians to assist clients on their path to full recovery. Contact work provided by a carer can support this and can also provide a lifeline for carers, a workable method of grounding the other person and maintaining contact at home to make everyday care more humane, and a rewarding relationship a possibility.

MOVING ON, WITH HOPE

Before my son entered the inner world of the mental health system he had difficulties. Five years later those original difficulties are still there and are now compounded with problems arising from NHS treatment and the professionals' ways of relating, which I consider to be tantamount to physical and emotional abuse. My son did not ask for this; he does not need this. And I feel betrayed.

By hanging on to my son by the merest thread with the help of Pre-Therapy contact reflections, he is now back home. Over the months within our supportive and caring environment, he is becoming more secure.

In public he is still incredibly vulnerable. His facial and body movements make him look odd. His life has been directed, controlled and dominated to such an extent that any vestige of self-empowerment has been scuppered. It is as though his very being does not belong to him any more. Any feelings of trust have long since disappeared. He is like an empty shell.

Only in an environment where professionals embrace other people by being open, upfront and genuine in their caring for others as members of humanity, do I believe my son would be in receipt of a healing relationship. Within his shell there remains a hidden pearl, which can be reached, touched and revealed as the person he truly is.

5

IN AND OUT OF CONTACT: THERAPY WITH PEOPLE IN THE 'GREY-ZONE'

Dion Van Werde coined the term 'grey-zone' (Van Werde 2002a, Van Werde, 2005 and Chapter 6, this volume) for the many cases involving people diagnosed with 'PSYCHOSIS' when the counsellor has the experience of sometimes being in good, mutual contact with the client, and, at other times, having no clue whatsoever about what is going on in the client. In the latter case, the counsellor can often feel that they might just as well be a fly on the wall or possibly that the client has no wish to communicate anything or has no wish to be understood by the counsellor. The client may be expressing something, but it seems inconsequential to the client whether the counsellor is attending to their expressions or not, and even less consequential whether or not the counsellor understands their expressions. When the counsellor feels out of contact with a client, the client might either seem unable to, or be uninterested in, making themselves understood to the counsellor. On the other hand, they may, mistakenly, take such understanding for granted.

In whatever role (counsellor, social worker, psychiatric nurse, psychotherapist, etc.) one is working with people diagnosed with a PSYCHOTIC condition, one will often have the experience of fluctuating between being in and out of contact with the client, particularly when working in what we might call an ordinary psychiatric setting, where most people diagnosed with a PSYCHOTIC condition function in Dion Van Werde's 'grey-zone'. The diagnosis of PSYCHOSIS, of whatever kind, does not *necessarily* exclude good mutual contact, but the counsellor's experience of 'good mutual contact' will more often be disrupted in work with such people than with people diagnosed with so-called 'personality disorders', 'NEUROSES' etc. and more 'minor' psychiatric distress.

When working with people in the grey-zone, the counsellor must fluctuate between the ordinary empathic reflectivity of client-centred therapy and the contact reflectivity of Pre-Therapy, depending on whether they feel in touch in the moment with what is going on 'under the skin' of the client or not. The more in touch they feel, the more the empathic reflectivity of client-centred therapy is appropriate; the less in touch they feel, the more the contact reflectivity of Pre-Therapy is appropriate.

The capacity to fluctuate between the empathic reflectivity of client-centred therapy and the contact reflectivity of Pre-Therapy can enhance the contact work of all kinds of professionals (not only counsellors and psychotherapists) with clients diagnosed with a PSYCHOTIC condition. This chapter, however, concentrates on the type of work which is characteristic of individual counselling or psychotherapy.

Traditionally, the most disturbed clients in psychiatry have been regarded by most schools of psychotherapy as being 'beyond therapeutic reach', since most therapeutic approaches normally demand some degree of cooperation from the potential client, (apart from permitting the therapist to be physically present). At the very least, therapists from most orientations depend on experiencing a minimal degree of client interest in, and ability to:

- keep a sustained focus of attention
- make him or herself understood by the therapist
- change something about him or herself
- receive and process input/interventions from the therapist's frame

For various reasons, though, therapists will not have these experiences with many of the most disturbed and distressed patients:

- FLORIDLY PSYCHOTIC patients rarely keep a sustained focus for any substantial length of time
- withdrawn, so-called AUTISTIC patients seem to have no wish to be understood by others
- people diagnosed with DELUSIONS of persecution apparently don't feel in need of help to change anything about themselves, they want the relevant authorities to put a halt to the persecution
- people diagnosed with DELUSIONS of grandiosity seem to think that it is everybody else who is in need of their help, not the

other way around
• people diagnosed with a PSYCHOTIC depression seem so depleted
    of energy and hope that they can't contribute anything to a
    therapeutic relationship
• people diagnosed with a manic PSYCHOSIS feel happily elated
    without any worries requiring a therapist's help

Furthermore, these patients are largely either incapable of, or
uninterested in, receiving input/interventions from the therapist's
frame (point of view). Since these are people whose behaviour is
almost always distressing and disruptive to others, they are
frequently involuntarily admitted to hospital (SECTIONED) and
medicated. Many of the *voluntary* treatments or offers of help,
for example, psychotherapy, are often refused, because they do
not feel there is anything psychologically wrong with them and
thus they do not feel in need of psychological help.

Of course, this list is a crude generalisation. It is stereotypical
and leaves out all the nuances and subtle degrees of difference in
these peoples' experiences and behaviour. Still, embedded in these
stereotypes lie the reasons these patients are normally considered
beyond psychotherapeutic reach. They are, however, not beyond
reach of client-centred therapy, most often in combination with
Pre-Therapy, due to the non-directive attitude of the client-centred
therapist and pre-therapist. A non-directive client-centred therapist
using Pre-Therapy will make no particular interventions in the
hope that they will be helpful to the client. Of course, the therapist
hopes that the relationship, in general, will benefit the client, but
in a very basic sense he or she meets the client with an offer of
interest rather than with an offer of *help*. The therapist tries to
experience the client's momentary psychological landscape as the
client experiences it; the therapist has no wish to change the client
in any way, only to get to know the client to the degree the client
allows it. The patients described above are usually hypersensitive
to other peoples' wishes to change them, and when they sense
such wishes in another they typically react with resistance and/or
withdrawal. They do not normally resist or withdraw, though, when
they are approached with a sincere interest in their world. When

approached like this, of course, they may put a limit to the contact, not because they are resistive or fearful of the contact as such, but because they have better things to do than to talk to the therapist. In fact, in many cases, they welcome the therapist's interest and some end up wanting the contact to continue because they feel helped by it and want further help. At this point the relationship has developed into an ordinary client-centred therapy relationship that is motivated by the client's wish for help.

In the grey-zone some clients are well enough to seek out psychotherapy on their own initiative. Others are not, and in these cases it is the therapist's desire to contact the client that 'fuels' the relationship in a sometimes very extended 'beginning'. This means that the therapist makes a purely unilateral decision to seek out the client at regular times and places that have the best chance of finding the client receptive and open to contact. In most psychiatric settings, in my experience, this is most often late in the afternoon, in the client's room in the ward. But in the beginning phase, the therapist must be prepared to go in vain, since the client may be off to buy drinks and snacks, to visit family or friends, and so on, especially since these activities will not have been scheduled by the ward staff. Later, though, if the client is catching on to the idea of contact with the therapist, they may eagerly be waiting for the therapist around the time the therapist normally shows up.

Even so, it can often be a long time before the client will be able to, or interested in, making and keeping anything like an 'appointment' to meet with the therapist in his or her consultation room at pre-scheduled times. Indeed the relationship with more disturbed grey-zone clients may never develop that far. Sometimes, before the relationship has developed that far, the client is discharged from psychiatric hospital to sheltered accommodation that may be beyond the remit or territory of the therapist. Sometimes, finally, the client ends up with a wish for an ordinary therapeutic relationship that will then turn into a self-managed therapeutic relationship with often the long-term aim of decreasing their dependence on any (professional) sheltered service. And finally, sometimes, the client really has found better things to do than spend time with the therapist.

What follows are two examples of individual, psychotherapeutic contact work in the grey-zone. One is with a client who was motivated to attend psychotherapy sessions of her own accord. The other is with a client for whom the idea of psychotherapy was beyond his grasp at the time, and so it was the therapist who initiated and upheld the contact. In both examples Situation Reflections, Body Reflections, Word-for-Word Reflections, Facial Reflections, Reiterative Reflections and Empathic Reflections are marked SR, BR, WWR, FR, RR and ER, respectively (or ER? to indicate a possible Empathic Reflection). The therapist follows no rules in responding with any particular kind of reflection, only her sense of what is in the moment-to-moment focus of the client's attention.

LILLIAN

Lillian is diagnosed with PARANOID SCHIZOPHRENIA. She is, however, functioning well enough to be actively motivated to attend psychotherapy and is able to make and keep appointments. She comes to the therapist's office for their pre-scheduled sessions. In their first three sessions she talks rather freely of her conviction that her new neighbours are out to kill her. Even if the content of her narrative is a PARANOID DELUSION, she reveals much of what is going on in her with respect to this particular personal conception of reality and the therapist is therefore able to respond almost exclusively with empathic reflections. In the fourth session, however, her condition has changed, all energy seems drained out of her, she sits with her head bent down so the therapist cannot see her face, and she does not start talking on her own initiative as she did in the former sessions. She sits like this for some minutes, and the therapist has no idea of what is going on in her.

T0: We sit in silence and you have bent your head down. (SR, BR)

L1: [*L stays in the same position for a while. Then she raises her head a little and takes both her hands to her head, pulling her hair and using her hair as 'handles' to shake her head.*]

T1: [*Mirroring her gesture*] You shake your head with your hair.

(BR)

L2: [*L lets her hands sink into her lap and turns to look at me with what to me seems like an expression of hopelessness in her face and eyes.*]

T2: You look hopeless? (FR)

L3: [*Looking down again*] Yes … I don't know.

T3: You said: "Yes", and "I don't know". (WWR)

L4: I don't know what to say—I'm so tired.

T4: Too tired even to talk, is that how you feel? (ER)

L5: Yes … yes.
[*There is a long pause, where T stays silent and L remains motionless, with her head bent down, as in the start of the session. Then the loud 'cock-a-doodle-doo!' of a nearby cock is heard and L raises her head and looks towards the window.*]

T5: You look up at the sound of the cock. (BR, SR)

L6: [*Turns towards me and smiles at me, and I smile at her.*]

T6: You looked up at the sound of the cock and now we smile at each other, and you look glad. (RR, SR, FR)

L7: We used to have lots of animals at home when I was a kid; cocks, too; sometimes they kept everybody awake [*giggles*].

T7: [*Smiling*] Feels good and funny, recalling that, right? (ER)

L8: Yes, [*looking sad*] I wish I could be there again.

T8: You look sad when you think of how you miss being at home as a kid. (FR, ER)

L9: Yes, I wish I had my family, I feel so lonely, and I don't know what to do, I'm scared of returning home.

T9: 'If I had a family to return home to, I wouldn't feel so lonely and scared', is that it? (ER)

L10: Yes, K [*her primary nurse*] proposed the other day that I try to go home to my apartment with her, one of these days, to see how it feels; I think they want me to go home soon.

T10: You think they see you as being ready to go home soon, but you don't feel ready at all. You feel they hurry you a bit? (ER)

L11: Yes, but I think I should try to go home with K.

T11: You feel you ought to give it a try? (ER)

L12: Yes, I really don't know what to do, how I shall manage at home. I'm not so scared of the neighbours anymore, but still,

maybe I'll do something that disturbs them, so they'll
complain about me to the janitor and have me thrown out of
the apartment, that's what I'm thinking about all the time.

T12:You just worry so much that you won't do things right at
home, that you'll somehow displease your neighbours? (ER)

L13:Maybe,—they have two children so they are four and I'm
alone, and their apartment is the same size as mine …

T13:Feels as if you haven't got the right to occupy that much
space when they have so little? (ER)

L14:I know I've got the right, of course, but still … I guess I feel
somehow guilty about it … But that's only … it's weighing
me down, the thoughts, they keep turning and turning around
in my head. [*Bends her head down and away again, saying
this.*]

T14:[*Again feeling somewhat out of contact with L*] You said
'It's weighing me down' and you bend your head. [WWR *of
the part of the client's statement that seemed most meaningful
to her combined with* BR.]

L15: [*After a long pause, almost inaudible*] I don't think I can go
home with K, do you think she will be annoyed with me?

T15:I don't know, I wish I could tell you for sure that she wouldn't
be, 'cause I guess you are really afraid to displease her?
[*Answer to L's question.* ER]

L16:Yes, she has done a lot for me and she offers to escort me
home, and then I can't even think of trying.

T16:Like there'd be nothing you'd wish more than to feel able to
accept her offer and feel helped by it, but instead you feel
burdened by it, is it something like that? (ER)

L17:Yes, very, and I don't know how to tell her.

From this point the therapist had, again, a steady sense of mutuality
in the contact with Lillian, and the therapist could thus receive
Lillian's continuing considerations of how she'd deal with K's offer
with the ordinary empathic reflectivity of client-centred therapy. In
this case, K's idea of escorting Lillian on a home visit had stimulated
a kind of crisis reaction in Lillian whereby she lost some of her
normally good contact functioning. Being received, in this phase,

with pre-therapeutic contact reflections helped Lillian back to her ordinary level of relatively good mutual contact with others. Particularly, Lillian regained her normally enjoyable contact with K with whom she managed to make an arrangement about home visits that was satisfactory to both of them.

SVEND

Svend is also diagnosed with PARANOID SCHIZOPHRENIA. He is, however, not nearly as well-functioning, with respect to contact, as Lillian. He rarely seeks contact with others, there seems to be nothing he wants others to understand about him and he expresses no need for help, psychotherapeutic or otherwise. He was admitted as a voluntary patient, letting himself, passively, be taken into hospital. The wish to enter a psychotherapeutic relationship with this client is not the client's wish; it is the therapist's wish, so the therapist is the one who takes the initiative to talk with Svend in his room on the ward. This excerpt is from the sixth session. After Svend has declared his willingness to talk with the therapist, the therapist clears a stack of clothes from a chair and sits down.

T0: I thought that maybe … if there was anything you might like to tell me today, about how you feel, and about your situation, how you look on it?

S1: [*In a very matter of fact, 'there's no discussing it', way*] I feel well.

T1: You say you feel well, and you look very determinedly at me. (WWR, FR)

S2: Yes, I feel well, and that's a fact.
     [*Pause, C looks down on his lap*]

T2: You say it's a fact you feel well, and now you look down and are quiet. (WWR, BR)

S3: Yes, I feel well when I drink coffee, juice, and things like that, but water is no good—and I've stopped eating.

T3: As long as you can drink something that tastes good you feel well, but you've lost your appetite? (ER?)

S4: Yes, and I also feel well because I'm now totally out of the church.

T4: It's a relief to be finally out of it. (ER)

S5: Yes, well, I'm not totally out of it, I still receive their newsletter, and I can't read it, it was a mistake that I joined the church, I'm confused about it—I have to tell them to stop sending the newsletter.

T5: The church was really too much, and now you need to get that newsletter off your back, that'll be a relief? (ER)

S6: Yes, that's it, I need to stop the newsletter and to have my mail delivered here, then I can feel fine—but I do feel fine here.

T6: You like to be here, and if you had these things settled you could enjoy it better, be more at ease? (ER)

S7: Yes, precisely, that would be nice.
[*Pause, C moves his head around in abrupt jerks, staring at different spots*]

T7: You turn your head this way and that way and look around. (BR)

S8: [*Grinding his teeth*] My father is Satan.

T8: You grind your teeth and say 'My father is Satan'. (FR, WWR)

S9. He has slaughtered my mother, he is the real Satan, and the Danes are his devils and devils' brood.

T9: He is the real Satan, because he has slaughtered your mother, and the Danes are his devils and devils' brood. (WWR)

S10: Not all Danes, people here are nice to me, but he has slaughtered my mother and if he does it again I'll slaughter him.

T10: You feel you'll slaughter him if … (WWR)
[*C interrupts eagerly and vehemently with his voice raising*]

S11: Yes, he has terrorised my mother all her life, psychological terror … her name is Maria, if Satan harmed Maria … Joseph would slaughter him, I'm Joseph.

T11: You say 'I'm Joseph' and you feel like you think Joseph would feel if Satan harmed Maria, is that it? (WWR, ER?)

S12: [*Nodding his head and smiling*] Yes, and I'm not afraid of Satan, I'm not afraid of anything.

T12: You smile at the thought that you are not afraid of Satan or … (FR, WWR)

S13: (interrupting): Yes, I'm not afraid, I'm glad of that, but why does he always have to be so rotten, last time he visited he brought some fruit from his back garden; it smelled awful and then I took a bite and it tasted hellish … I threw it all away.

T13: You think that everything he brings … (ER?)

S14: (interrupting): Yes, why does he have to be so provocative?

T14: Like 'Why the hell can't you buy me some good fruit that I like, instead of bringing me the rotten leftovers from your back garden?' (ER)

S15: Yes, I think he never spreads anything but shit around him— I can't bear being near him.

The client spends the rest of the session exploring his relationship with his father in a way that seems much more coherent and less infiltrated with PSYCHOTIC IDEATION than in the first part of the session and in a way that makes empathic reflections more appropriate than contact reflections. When the client and the therapist part, Svend heads towards the nurses' office to secure their help with resigning his membership of the rather fundamentalist religious sect of which he has been a member. Thus, during the session his reality function, in particular, improved. It should be noted, however, that such improvement is rarely lasting with clients like Svend. Ordinarily, the next session will start on more or less the same level of contact functioning as the previous one and improvement is at best of the 'three steps forward and two steps back' variety. More steady improvement takes a very long time to achieve (in many cases, years), so a capacity *sine qua non* of the therapist is patience and still more patience. However, no matter how patient, it is the rare therapist who will not sometimes despair, lose confidence in themselves, and fail to see the often very subtle signs of progress. It is therefore important that the therapist has access to a supervisor and possibly support group that understands what the therapist is trying to accomplish.

In the transcribed session with Svend, it is characteristic that he jumps from one issue to the next without the therapist seeing any connection between the issues of feeling well, his drinking habits, the church and his father. This is typical of work with clients like Svend, with whom the therapist must tolerate the lack of apparent links between the issues the client touches upon. It is vital that the therapist does not hold on to a particular issue in order to satisfy their own wish for coherence and understanding of the connection between one issue and the next.

Readers might also note therapist response T11. This is really a bad response, clumsy, long-winded and too abstract. At this point the therapist momentarily lost her full concentration on the client's perspective. A mental picture of Svend killing his father disturbed the therapist's concentration and had scared her momentarily. Thus, in her response, she distanced herself from the full intensity and vehemence of the client's statement. Perhaps S12 shows that the client picked up the therapist's feeling of fear. A much better response would have been: 'I'm Joseph, I'll slaughter him if he harms Maria', stated with some of the client's intensity. However, the therapist regains her full concentration and poise in the following responses, and the poor response doesn't seem to influence the client's progress to better reality contact towards the end of the session. Therapists are fallible, and if their failures are the exception rather than the rule, they normally do not influence the process in any significantly negative way.

Although the situations described in this chapter are from a psychiatric setting, it is the case that clients in a wide range of counselling and psychotherapy settings will be functioning in the grey-zone. Similarly, carers and support workers will find people in the grey-zone struggling to maintain good contact. They will move in and out of contact; making many day-to-day activities, as well as much therapeutic work, a matter of trial and error unless they are approached in way that focuses on their communicative state and offers contact reflections as a matter of course when people seem 'out of contact'. In the next chapter we shall extend these ideas from one-to-one relationships to an institutional setting.

6

CONTACT WORK IN A RESIDENTIAL PSYCHIATRIC SETTING: BRIDGING PERSON, TEAM AND CONTEXT

In this chapter I will look back over 20 years of practice and try to formulate the essentials of what, in my eyes, constitutes a person-centred Pre-Therapy ward MILIEU. Much of this has been described in Prouty, Van Werde & Pörtner (2002: 61–120), but here I will explain the general points and the logic of our reasoning behind the project.

We consider PSYCHOTIC functioning to be a human condition characterised by being locked or caught in a 'psychological bunker', from where consciousness no longer reaches out. This means that there is no relatedness with the person's own AFFECTIVE functioning, other people or surrounding reality. It is a state Gendlin (1964) called 'frozen functioning'. Although seemingly safe, the person who is locked in will 'psychologically die' from this condition since the normal human process of existing through relating and feeling is endangered. Implicitly, this kind of functioning can be seen as a quest for help and contact—as described by Prouty—and can function as an antidote for this PSYCHOTIC ALIENATION. Contact is offered since it is the interpersonal quality directly but inversely related to symptoms of PSYCHOSIS. More contact is required to touch deeper PSYCHOTIC functioning. Put simply, more contact means less PSYCHOTIC functioning.

Now we will look at what this means for the daily practice of acute psychiatric residential care, where we are facing an *individual* coming to us in the *context* of a ward setting that we deal with in a *multi-disciplinary* way. This implies several things.

CONTEXT

The client/patient is always situated in a context, and so is the caregiver. The latter is defined by the practicalities of the profession, the tasks the caregiver has to fulfil, decisions about managing one's time/work schedule, one's place in the hierarchy and so on.

In terms of residential care, it also concerns, for example, the responsibilities and tasks of being a nurse, motivating people to participate in therapies, to have patients make their beds, come to lunch on time, respect the ward rules and so on. One also shares the responsibility for the physical safety of the patient/client and for the other people on the ward in general.

However desirable it might appear at first glance, it is clear that your attention must not solely be on the individual's inner process. So, for example, it would be inappropriate to progress with someone's psychotherapeutic process if it means him screaming and running around, since it would be threatening to the sometimes fragile balance and well-being of the other clients on the ward. Nor, for example, could you let the patient go home if he was admitted to hospital as an 'involuntary patient' as a result of a SECTION. These situations necessarily constrain the helper.

So, in each INTERVENTION, you have to bridge sometimes opposing interests—limitations have to be taken into account if you want to work with the process, given the defined boundaries. It is a matter of working consciously and not getting carried away by being exclusively focused on the client's experiencing to the exclusion of all else. On the other hand, it can also mean picking up the responsibility for organising some space and appropriate staff to facilitate the individual's progress in his psychological/ psychotherapeutic process, without being hindered too much by house rules, timetables and other external demands and limitations. It is a question of balancing competing needs.

In any case, it is always important to realise how much room to manoeuvre you as a caregiver have yourself, and where on the continuum 'structure versus process' you are situated. It takes some skill to include attention for the individual's process, even when working at the near opposite end of the continuum where the most attention is given to having somebody fit the structure. This really demands a 'HOLISTIC eye' and the skill of being able to translate your intentions into a concrete INTERVENTION that covers both ends where possible.

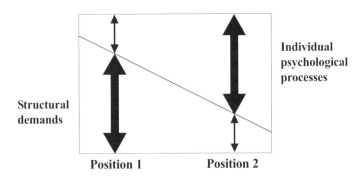

Figure 1: A continuum specified by a blend of two extreme factors always involved in daily care: structural demands versus individual psychological process.

At Position 1: *Many structural demands and limitations to be met.* Almost no space for working with the person's individual process is left.
At Position 2: *The individual's psychological process as main focus.* Almost no structural or context factors play a role at this position on the continuum.

There are always 'reality demands' in play, even when working quasi-exclusively with psychological process, but there probably will always be at least *some* small space left to address individual process when acting within an externally defined framework. Even in a Pre-Therapy session, with the therapist's attention predominantly focused on the pre-expressively surfacing inner process, the reality that I have to catch the 6 o'clock bus home can also play a role.

Suppose somebody enters the nurses' office for the fifth time without knocking at the door. What do you do? Do you harshly tell them to 'go out and behave properly', concerned only with the house rules? Or do you manage to look further and notice a worried face and degree of desperation in the way she repeatedly asks the same question? Your response to the situation will be influenced if you take these process elements into account. Then, you may not only reflect the fact that she entered the room (Situational Reflection), but add that her face looks puzzled (Facial Reflection), and that she has been asking the same question (Reiterative Reflection) now for the fifth time. Maybe as a consequence, she can then start to realise that she is indeed very worried, and that her worries are preoccupying her to the extent that she loses track of what exactly she has already done about it. It is likely that she only pre-expressively 'knows' she wants help, and obviously came to the people she can expect it from: the nurses. Perhaps the step from pre-expressive worrying to this heightened awareness finally makes a conversation possible. The client/patient may then be able to be comforted about her worries, so that further unannounced entering and this 'unadjusted' and 'problematic' looking for help ceases. Furthermore, it is possible that the nurse might continue her INTERVENTION and go with the patient to her room to spend some time together. Another constructive possibility could involve the patient being asked to give a hand in the kitchen when drinks at coffee time are being prepared, to root her further in the daily routine and thus secure her regained contact level and not let her be drawn into her idiosyncratic worries again.

It is a matter of picking a strategy for the individual and situation at hand, and being reflective (and sometimes critical) about your actions. Telling the woman to go out and behave properly ('knock first, please') is simply too instructional, crude and possibly punishing. It ignores the context and everything that is happening at that given moment and isn't appropriate if you want to *meet* this woman. A combined and integrated paying attention and listening to the context as well as to the client will have a better chance of helping her take a new step in her recovery and help her be in command of her own situation again.

Sometimes, when an acute crisis is pending, there will be little or no opportunity for this kind of intervention because the helper has to act first and foremost within the defined external structure and limitations. For example, if somebody wants to run away or starts to be aggressive, it might nevertheless be possible to combine your behavioural intervention (restraint) with reflecting what you are doing. If you are on your way to restraining or securing somebody, you can only add reflections to make the situation more transparent by saying, for example, 'you are making a lot of noise', 'we are here to take you to your room', 'I'm taking you by the arm and leading you to your room, now' whilst still acting as planned. Although there may be practically no opportunity for educative or therapeutic processes, contact can still be maintained, and the possibilities are then kept open.

Essentially in this HUMANISTIC positive psychological approach, we are trying to preserve an EXISTENTIAL point of view *at all times.* By this I mean that we have to develop a strategy to overcome the supposed antithesis between choosing to work on the one hand with the patient's (possibly disruptive) behaviour, or on the other, with his individual psychotherapeutic process. Because there are two opposites involved doesn't mean that you have to choose one to the exclusion of the other. You work with the phenomena as they behaviourally present themselves *at the same time as* working relationally and EXPERIENTIALLY with the client's inner realities. Preferably, even in the example given, you work with both sides of the same coin at the same time (there is more on this in the section 'contact work in practice' later in this chapter).

WORKING WITH A PERSON'S PSYCHOTHERAPEUTIC PROCESS

When systematic and intensive psychological care of PSYCHOTIC functioning is absolutely necessary because PSYCHOTIC material is surfacing in the present moment, Pre-Therapy as a specific INTERVENTION is needed to restore psychological contact with the surrounding world, the client's own affective life, and other people. This kind of work is best done by a practitioner specifically trained in Pre-Therapy and there are several case descriptions in the existing literature (Prouty, 1998; Prouty, Van Werde & Pörtner, 2002; Krietemeyer & Prouty, 2003).

In the life of the patient, PSYCHOSIS has become the foreground and everyday living, the background. Pre-Therapy helps return everyday living to the foreground. As soon as the PSYCHOSIS retires to the background, and the patient again can function in an open ward with the traditional therapies offered to him, the helper can shift towards strengthening the restored, but still fragile, contact functioning. Many procedures can be offered in combination, around the clock. We will look at some concrete examples of this multidisciplinary contact work later in the chapter.

In our own experience in residential acute psychiatry, difficult situations arise when somebody temporarily falls back into PSYCHOTIC functioning, even though they are on their way to recovery. We conceptualised this as 'grey-zone functioning', meaning that somebody functions 'in between' PSYCHOTIC and so-called 'anchored' or 'normal' functioning. It is having one foot in the shared reality and one foot in the idiosyncratic reality.

In these circumstances, patients are not deeply or pervasively PSYCHOTIC anymore, so they again can understand and pay attention to what is being offered, but they are not yet so anchored in the shared reality that they can fully master their own further recovery and are ready to leave the hospital. The therapeutic challenge then can be formulated as being about picking up and working with this edgy, mixed and by definition, confusing functioning, by anchoring the client back in the shared reality. Only after this, can one then proceed to strengthening this regained contact further. We will look at an example of how to do this in practice below.

A MULTIDISCIPLINARY APPROACH

Moments of contact loss are exactly the situations that therapists and nurses on our ward run into frequently. Since contact and PSYCHOTIC functioning are directly but inversely related, this means that once contact is established and the still fragile functioning is slowly strengthened, PSYCHOTIC functioning will continue to decrease. We designed the ward interpersonal environment to enhance this process of shifting the balance in favour of 'anchored' functioning. On a day-to-day basis in the ward, each professional caregiver delivers their services in ways that are aimed at enhancing further contact functioning. The physiotherapist does this by doing body work, the occupational therapist does this by using various materials and exercises, the music therapist, for example, invites patients to improvise together, nurses and support workers invite patients to make the beds, talk about non-threatening subjects together, and have them assist in the housekeeping, whilst the psychologist has individual conversations, and so on.

What is possibly innovative is how contact work has been built in systematically to some of the activities we organise. For example, the ward psychologist runs a weekly group session where people are introduced to the PHENOMENOLOGICAL approach. In each session, after a short introduction an exercise is presented, such as asking participants to have a conversation in pairs, with the explicit instruction to do it in the format of an interview. 'A' chooses a subject that has nothing to do with his problems and then is interviewed by 'B'. 'B' has to be interested by the subject and must restrict himself to only asking questions. Once one or both realise that the conversation is drifting away towards talking about problems instead of asking and responding to subject-based questions, they have to correct themselves and go back to the agreed structure of the exercise. After a while they switch roles. In this playful and innocent way, they learn:

- to choose a topic, putting their problems aside, correcting their position if necessary and thus try to master their inner world again
- to concentrate on sticking to one topic
- that they have to be communicative about it
- that by being interested and open, and by asking questions, they start to learn about the subject under discussion and the person doing the talking

This is the process of getting acquainted with, and learning about, non-prejudiced receptiveness within well-defined and secure boundaries. Patients can transfer the benefit from this 'attitude of applied PHENOMENOLOGY' to the times when listening to—and thus learning about—their voices or to their depressive feelings, but also to such things as when appreciating art or having a good conversation with a friend on a non-threatening topic.

The same attitude is achieved by having a walk in the autumn to look for mushrooms in the hospital grounds. After 15 minutes walking around by themselves, we make a tour together to look at the different mushrooms they have chosen. Each one presents his mushroom to the others by describing some visual characteristics of it. In the end, we all learn about the differences and characteristics of the rich variety present. The week after, we do this a second time and notice how things have—often surprisingly—changed. When returning to the ward for coffee after these kinds of contact strengthening sessions, we usually get feedback from the nurses that everybody looks very much alive. Indeed, this simple activity brings back some energy previously thought to be lost—quite the opposite of the sedative effect of some medications.

In another group offer of five consecutive sessions, each of the senses is systematically addressed and exercised. The idea is that strengthening the possibilities for correct perception is beneficial to counter the burden of having to deal with DELUSIONAL or hallucinatory experiencing. Participants might do tastings, go out to listen to sounds nearby, further and further away and then make an inventory of what everybody has heard. All perceptions are equally welcomed and 'put on the table' but it can be confronting when, for example, one person in the group is the only one who heard his (deceased) mother talk to him. You notice the feel of non-judgemental acceptance, of welcoming interest, precision, and the respect and importance given to the realities present. All are essential in this way of working and testify to the general attitude we value on our ward. More examples are given in Prouty, Van Werde and Pörtner (2002) of how to integrate this way of thinking and working in terms of organising the weekly ward meeting, interior design of the ward and putting together leisure activities.

CONTACT WORK IN PRACTICE

What we learned by translating Pre-Therapy into a ward approach was how to conceptualise and position the work of the nurses, support workers and, in fact, of everybody and anything that happens on the ward. The importance of the effect of Pre-Therapy became apparent as we discovered how non-verbal therapies, the material environment and the whole treatment programme can be organised to fit the concept of organising a 'contact MILIEU'.

I now offer an example to illustrate how we work to bring

together all of the issues mentioned so far. It is about working with the *person's* psychological process, dealing with it in a multidisciplinary *team approach*, given one's own professional role and agenda, and doing this within the *context* of the formal structures of the service we work in.

The example concerns a nurse (who is a member of a multi-disciplinary *team*) visiting a patient who has remained motionless in her room for hours. The nurse wants to find out why the patient wasn't at the coffee break and if the patient has already decided what to do about leaving the hospital for the weekend, i.e. the nurse was confronted with this *person's* concrete behaviour as well as the *person's* psychological process. The nurse—being situated in the context of a ward setting with its rules, routines and tasks to fulfil—needs to know, since she must order the right number of meals for the next few days on the ward.

The nurse, in following the client's level of functioning, decides to try to make contact first, and only then proceed with her questions about the forthcoming weekend.

You will see how the whole interaction stays focused on the very concrete here and now, and matches the actual level of functioning of the patient. In this example, the nurse sometimes uses Pre-Therapy reflections. When she thinks the client's level can stand it, she goes a small step further by asking a question or giving a comment. As you will read, as a result of the contact work, the nurse avoids being cornered and paralysed by the two extreme choices she seems to face. Neither does she choose one, i.e. the structure (just making a remark commenting on the absence at coffee break and then asking a straightforward question about the weekend) or the other, i.e. choosing to follow the psychological process (just being interested in, and maybe drawn into what is psychologically happening 'inside' the silent and non-responsive patient). In our example, the nurse manages to bridge this dilemma by the contact work she does.

Vignette: Making arrangements for the coming weekend

The nurse enters the room of Ann (patient) to call her for the coffee break where she is expected. A bridge has to be built between the patient who sits alone in her room, and ward life. On the one hand, if we look at the situation from the psychological process side, Ann looks frozen, doesn't react to a directly asked question and has been sitting in her room like this for hours. On the other hand, if we look at it from the 'external structure and rules' side, being admitted on to the ward means that the patient has accepted responsibility to do certain things like drinking coffee together, participating in the offered therapies and responding to questions the nurses ask concerning, for example, the arrangements made for the coming weekend. So, what is the nurse to do?

The nurse tries to bridge both sides of the given situation by making contact with Ann first, and then introducing her nurse's agenda of asking about her the plans for the weekend.

The reflections or first tentative questions can be about something concrete and whilst peripheral to the nurse's agenda, are at the centre of the concrete shared reality. Such tentative initial reflections could include, for example, what the nurse sees when following the client's gaze through the window: 'people are walking outside' (SR); 'it has started raining again' (SR). Or regarding something that happened just before this encounter (RR): 'at noon, I came to get you and you were sitting exactly as you are sitting now'; or 'did your son give you his little teddy bear that you are holding in your hand now, to take with you to the hospital?' Sometimes the client herself is addressed, be it her body position (BR): 'your elbow is on the table', 'you were sitting like at noon'; the expression of her face (FR): 'you sigh …', 'it looks like you're thinking …'; or reflecting the words she starts to speak (WWR): 'letting go hurts …', 'I can't let it go, mustn't ever let it go'.

The facial reflection 'you sigh' in our example opens the door to Ann contacting and expressing feeling. She thaws a little bit and makes eye contact. Her contact level increases and makes a question-and-answer interaction possible. The nurse asks about the arrangements made for the weekend. They finally can talk about it, and the nurse gets the information he needed. The client now leaves her corner by the bed, and they can go to the living room together for coffee.

CONCLUSION

In this approach, the client isn't reduced to either psychological process or behaviour. We try to work with both aspects of the same reality at the same time. This demands a highly disciplined way of working with people. It is easy to fall back to one of the extreme positions. It is therefore important to be able to see the context of our efforts and see what contribution we might be able to make given (a) our place in the multidisciplinary net of care and (b) the level of functioning of this particular client.

We have seen the value of an idea that—although simple at first sight—is able to inspire every essential action that is undertaken in the ward, be it towards clients, colleagues, or one's own experiences.

A frequently asked question is about how to introduce, establish and keep alive and fresh Pre-Therapy and the concept of a contact MILIEU, within an already well-established way of working in an orthodox medical environment.

This approach isn't very expert-oriented or 'fancy'; nor is it widespread in the various layers of professional or volunteer caregiving. Ideally, one needs to have an 'inside person' who is passionate about the whole thing, who wants to carry the project of introducing it, and who has enough resources to keep him or herself going. It will require intellectual, emotional and physical stamina.

As soon as people begin to work with clients using Pre-Therapy, they will easily come to recognise the relevance of the approach, since it often is very compatible with their own intuitive good practice. The use of contact reflections and the spirit of contact work in general can be compared with how one naturally behaves towards young children. When they make their first efforts to communicate or to relate to the environment, everybody is thrilled and careful not to rush them, or be to demanding. One is respectful and receptive to whatever is expressed, since that guarantees the most beneficial development of latent capacities.

If you are interested in applying Pre-Therapy and contact work to a ward situation, you can find more information by following the suggestions for further reading on page 110. Talk about your work with colleagues and think about joining the Pre-Therapy International Network (see p. 110) to learn about workshops run by experienced members of the Network who stay in touch with Garry Prouty and the Pre-Therapy movement.

What is simultaneously surprising and dramatically relevant is that everything that has been described isn't only about working with people who suffer PSYCHOSIS. The attitudes constituting a contact MILIEU are also 'productive' in working within the organisation and for managing the personnel. Also in daily interactions, it is important not to be solely interested in limitations, products, rules, tasks and so on. If we fail to make contact with each other person-to-person, work is so much more difficult to get done. It is easy to behave in a way which results in members of staff feeling put off and dismissed as people, when neither their intentions, nor themselves as people, have been seen and acknowledged. If someone is reprimanded every time they misunderstand a question, they are made to feel totally inadequate and marginalised.

Translated to a helper–patient relationship, you can imagine what courage it takes, when still functioning in the grey-zone, but nevertheless struggling to express oneself or trying to function in formal structures, ward meetings, coffee breaks or therapy sessions, etc. Needless to say, a welcoming attitude from staff is essential for patients to psychologically even survive. They each need to be listened to as a person. Being functional, task centered and structure-fitting is only a part of that.

Due to the non-evaluative and interested listening to one another, the other is able to show himself and really be the one he is. We call this the result of a PHENOMENOLOGICAL basic attitude (Deleu & Van Werde, 1998). It applies to everything:
- to the listening to your voices that don't make sense to you
- to listening to your communication that I don't really understand
- to the story behind the mistake the nurse made when doing something that she thought was right, and so on

In that sense, these apparently diverse activities of Pre-Therapy with PSYCHOTIC functioning, contact work, empathic listening and working with staff are not all that different.

7

PRE-THERAPY, CONTACT WORK
AND DEMENTIA CARE

INTRODUCTION

The World Health Organisation *ICD-10* (1992) defines dementia as:

> … a syndrome due to disease of the brain, usually of a chronic or progressive nature, in which there is a disturbance of multiple higher cortical functions, including memory, thinking, orientation, comprehension, calculation, learning capacity, language and judgment. Consciousness is not clouded. Impairments of cognitive functioning are commonly accompanied, and occasionally preceded, by deterioration in emotional control, social behaviour or motivation.

The term includes specific types of dementia such as Alzheimer's Disease, Vascular dementia, and Lewy Body dementia. When suffering from dementia, people are commonly forgetful, particularly about recent events. They have difficulty in handling complex tasks and show behaviours such as walking and restlessness. They may experience hallucinations and have difficulty expressing themselves and understanding others. In later stages people may be unable to maintain personal hygiene, may respond in self-protective ways that are aggressive, or withdraw from others. Speech and language also changes, becoming more disjointed and difficult for others to understand (Rabins, Lyketsos & Steele, 2006). Speech patterns of people with dementia often appear more poetic or metaphorical and consequently staff are sometimes left floundering about how to respond (Killick, 2002). Sufferers experience greater disorientation and confusion, they may believe that they are living in the past and their understanding of their surroundings may change.

It is likely that a large number of people reading this will have had a family member with dementia and will appreciate that the cognitive changes differ from person to person. A psychosocial model of dementia views the NEUROLOGICAL and COGNITIVE changes in relation to a person's personality, life history, relationships with others and their environment (Keady, 2006). Combining a medical with a psychosocial perspective helps us see the effects of dementia on individuals differ from person to person. For example in the later stages one person may become withdrawn and restless, another may become more accusing and distressed.

Dementia is a complex mental health issue. It is understood by looking at the interplay of:
- NEUROLOGICAL and COGNITIVE changes
- physical health
- personality
- life history
- previous ways of coping
- environment
- social relationships

Rather confusingly, therapeutic approaches in dementia care have been called 'person-centred' approaches. By adopting this broad term, 'person-centred dementia care' has come to mean seeing the person, rather than a task or an object; valuing the unique subjective experiences of the person with dementia and the importance of their relationships with others; focusing on how a person with dementia might retain their sense of self in the face of a dementing process which interferes with their ability to express themselves (McCormack, 2004; Kontos, 2005). As a result 'person-centred approaches' in dementia care acts as an umbrella term for a whole range of approaches which are broadly person-focused, although they are often termed person-centred. This is possibly confusing since, for people working in counselling or psychotherapy, the term 'person-centred' refers to a particular Rogerian approach (Sanders, 2006). For the purposes of this book, the term 'person-focused approaches' in dementia care is used, to avoid confusion.

PERSON-FOCUSED APPROACHES IN DEMENTIA CARE

In order to help readers locate the use of contact reflections in the progressive nature of dementia I will first outline some of the person-focused approaches in dementia care. In the brief summary below, some of these approaches have been rather artificially divided into early and later stages of dementia. Some approaches are appropriate throughout the dementing process (such as activity, REMINISCENCE); others are more specific to the capacity of the person with dementia (such as MEMORY RETRAINING). Specific approaches are tailored to the COGNITIVE ability and the individual needs of the person.

Figure 1.

Severity of dementing process	Examples of approaches in dementia care
Early stages	• COGNITIVE BEHAVIOURAL APPROACHES focusing on understanding, reframing and coping with the onset of dementia • MEMORY RETRAINING and MEMORY ENHANCEMENT
Moderate stages	• REMINISCENCE—enhancing self-esteem and reliving positive memories • Identity work and biographical work—enhancing self-identity, roles and relationships • Loss work—working with the aspects of grief arising for the person with dementia • Activity based care—useful in all stages of dementia to promote well-being, use of abilities and enjoyment, for example, art, dance, hobbies
More severe stages	• VALIDATION THERAPY—entering into the world and reality of the person with dementia, resolution of past conflicts • RESOLUTION THERAPY—understanding the meaning behind confused behaviour as a way the person with dementia is coping with the present
In later stages	• Sensory approaches—using media which rely less on language and engage people in movement, music, touch, etc.

Those interested in communication with people with dementia may find the work of John Killick and Tom Kitwood useful (e.g. Killick & Allan, 2001; Kitwood, 1997). Many mainstream approaches have a humanist foundation and much of the current dementia literature rests on the moral imperative to engage with the humanness of people with dementia, in order to counteract NEUROLOGICAL changes that may get in the way of a person's ability to express their own sense of personhood. Kitwood (1997), in particular, draws attention to relationships between the person with dementia and the worker, with the aim of providing people with dementia greater opportunities for positive social and emotional experiences that may counteract some of the detrimental effects of the typical care environments and social interactions that surround them. As a result, the personhood of the individual with dementia is strengthened as workers focus on providing a variety of opportunities for positive constructive social interactions.

PRE-THERAPY AND DEMENTIA CARE

The application of Pre-Therapy to dementia is relatively new (Van Werde, 2002b; Dodds, Morton & Prouty, 2004). Van Werde and Morton (1996) first introduced it within an overview of person-centred approaches in dementia care, seeing that it has the potential to offer 'emotional palliative care' (Morton, 1996). The progressive NEUROLOGICAL and COGNITIVE changes mean that a person with dementia is not going to recover and progress to traditional psychotherapy; however, the contact reflections hold the potential to maximise the opportunity for a person to express themselves, and enhance the moments of lucidity and the engagement with the worker on an empathic level. Below is an example of the contact reflections used with a man who is in a residential facility. He spends a large part of his day walking around the ward, he often behaves aggressively to staff and other residents. Due to the dementia, his ability to communicate verbally is extremely impaired and he is usually silent. Much of his day is spent in isolation from others and the majority of his contact with staff is focused on practical tasks such as washing, dressing, eating.

At the time of this interaction he was walking in the corridor, his eyes did not appear to be focused on anything in particular and he was walking slowly without any discernable purpose. At the beginning of the interaction he was approached slowly and, using the same pace and rhythm of his walking, the nurse began to walk alongside him. The nurse stays slightly ahead so that he can see that there is another person with him, as he often seems unaware of the presence of others around him. He was walking next to the wall and the nurse was in the middle of the corridor. This extract contains the dialogue and events that occurred in addition to notes on the use of the contact reflections. It shows how contact between Mr X and the nurse was slowly built.

Nurse: 'We're walking.' (BR)
[*This is a body reflection, however the nurse also reflects the movements non-verbally, emphasising the postures and movements of walking.*]
Mr X: [Mr X continues walking, making no eye contact, no change in behaviour.]
Nurse: 'The rail is there.' (SR)
[The nurse reaches across and touches the rail. *Whilst this may seem intrusive, there is a need to provide greater visual and non-verbal cues for people with dementia as the capacity to comprehend language may be severely impaired.*]
Mr X: [Mr X continues walking, making no eye contact, no change in behaviour.]
Nurse: 'We're walking, your hands by your side … the rail.' (SR, BR, SR)
[*Again the situational reflections of walking and the rail are enhanced by the nurse physically gesturing walking and touching the rail. The body reflection of his hands being by his side is also enhanced non-verbally by the nurse mirroring this movement.*]
Mr X: [The resident continues walking, making no eye contact, no change in behaviour.]
Nurse: 'The wall is here.' (SR)

[The nurse touches the wall. *The situational reflections of the rail and the wall involve the nurse reaching over and in front of the resident to touch them. This interrupts the field of vision of the resident. Again this could be seen as disrupting the world of the person, however, it still stands as an invitation for the person with dementia by drawing attention to the environment. In this way the worker is also placing their own body in the environment of the person with dementia and this itself may result in the person with dementia noticing the worker.*]

Mr X: [Mr X looks at the nurse's hand.]

Nurse: 'Is here, you look at my hand on the wall.' (SR)
[*Here we see that Mr X has started to notice the nurse's hand on the wall.*]

Mr X: [Mr X continues walking.]

Nurse: 'We're walking, your face is down.' (SR, FR)
[The nurse continues to mirror the body posture and movements of Mr X. The nurse also non-verbally reflects his facial expression. This involves the nurse walking ahead and slightly turned towards Mr X, so that her face is within his field of vision.]

Mr X: [Mr X touches the wall.]

Nurse: 'We're touching the wall, we're looking.' (SR)
[Repeats the movement of touching the wall.]

Mr X: [Continues to touch the wall.]

Nurse: 'A picture here.' (SR)
[The nurse touches the edge of the picture frame, running her hand up and down the frame.]

Mr X: [Mr X touches the frame.]

Nurse: 'Your hand on the frame.' (SR)

Mr X: [Looks at the picture and looks at the nurse. *Here we see the building of contact as he is more in contact with the environment (the wall, picture) and with the nurse (by looking at her face).*]

Nurse: 'You look at me and the picture.' (FR, SR)
[*The nurse strengthens the contact.*]

Mr X: [Mr X then touches the image on the picture which is of

a tiger, he then looks at the nurse and goes 'GRRRRR'
and smiles. The image in the picture is a tiger.]

Suspending assumptions of meaning

As a rule of thumb it may be useful to suspend assumptions that the
person with dementia may recognise an object, e.g. a cardigan may
not be seen as a cardigan but as a duster, therefore we have to
engage with the meaning of the object *to the person*. Similarly
objects in the environment may not exist in the same reality to the
worker and the person with dementia. Flowers may be flowers on
the windowsill of a ward to staff, but may represent the flowers on
their relative's grave to the person with dementia. It is also difficult
to know the meaning of the person's behaviour, e.g., someone
walking around may be looking for the toilet, but unable to tell us,
or they may be looking for a dead relative, or they may be looking
for the way out because they believe they have to go home. We also
have to accommodate the possible visiospatial difficulties that can
arise with dementia—the perceptual field of a person may change.
A common example of this is seeing a person with dementia trying
to 'step over' a point where the colour of a carpet changes, as if
they are seeing this as a step, rather than a change in the colour of a
flat surface. Pre-Therapy contact reflections allow us the opportunity
to suspend assumptions. By offering no interpretation of what the
person is seeing, doing or feeling, we simply reflect in a way that
engages at the level of meaning to the person with dementia.

Working with the non-verbal

Working with people with dementia involves extensive use of non-
verbal contact reflections. This mainly comes from the difficulties
in language that accompany the dementing process. We are in the
difficult position of not knowing precisely whether someone is
unable to understand the words we say to them because the ORGANIC
changes may have affected the person's ability to recognise and
process words. In addition we are more likely to use vague pronouns

like *it, here, them,* than factual concrete reflections. Again this is because we do not know whether the person has the cognitive capacity to know that what we see has the same meaning to the person with dementia. In the extract above, the nurse uses the correct nouns for rail, picture, however it would be equally useful to say *it.* One solution to these and other language dilemmas is the use of non-verbal movements by the nurse in the example above when they use a situational reflection (the rail), by touching the rail themselves. Where there is little response to correct nouns it is probably more useful to use more general terms or no language at all and rely solely on non-verbal communication. In dementia, the capacity to read and respond to non-verbal communication is retained much longer than the ability to use and understand language, so by focusing on non-verbal communication we are using the retained strengths and abilities of the person. Non-verbal reflections can be used to strengthen or even replace verbal contact reflections. In this way the work is much more 'embodied' for the worker, and requires physical empathy. This is also demonstrated by the greater use of combined verbal and non-verbal reflections, since by using two modes of reflection they are offering a stronger reflection to the person.

Illustrative example: *Mr A is looking frustrated, his facial expression displays aggravation, his brow is furrowed and his mouth is set tight. Knowledge of the person indicates that this expression is one of frustration and aggravation which can sometimes escalate into behaviour of becoming restless. In response to this the worker may initially offer a verbal facial reflection—'your brow is furrowed'. However, in dementia the over-reliance on language and comprehension by the worker may not maximise the opportunity for a contact behaviour and engagement. Then the worker may strengthen this reflection by adding a non-verbal facial reflection by subtly mirroring the facial expression of the person. A third level of strengthening is done by the worker doing a non-verbal bodily reflection and gesturing a shrug and 'huffing' which empathically reflect the frustration that the person with dementia is apparently experiencing.*

Considering other limited abilities

Working with older people requires being sensitive to other physical abilities that may be limited such as sight, hearing and mobility. This has important implications when offering contact reflections. If, for example, you were using situational reflections about the sun shining through the window, you must first be sure that the person can actually see the window. Also, they may have difficulty hearing verbal reflections so carers and nurses need to take basic steps to speak clearly, slowly and in a low tone so that the people we are working with can hear them. With the added difficulty of dementia whereby the person might not recognise the worker or understand the words he or she is saying, the worker needs to adopt the general principles of:

- taking sufficient time in offering reflections
- approaching the person slowly and gently
- making sure that they can see our faces
- being close enough that the person is aware of our presence

As a result, in dementia care we frequently work in much closer proximity with more physical contact than other client groups. With many (but not all) people with dementia, physical closeness and gentle touch is appreciated.

POTENTIAL DIFFICULTIES OF USING CONTACT REFLECTIONS WITH PEOPLE WITH DEMENTIA

Is the person pre-expressive?

As we have already seen, the nature of dementia care means that there are some special challenges to using contact reflections, such as the difficulty of knowing what words to use and not knowing the subtle effects of the dementing process on the person's capacity for language and comprehension. These special considerations are linked to a further difficulty for workers—not knowing if a person is 'pre-expressive' (see pp. 25–7) or 'disoriented'. Contact work is aimed at people in pre-expressive states, yet people with dementia are frequently highly expressive and 'relation seeking'. The damage to language and cognitive functioning, however leads to this being articulated in a way that can be difficult for staff to understand, or may appear to be pre-expressive. Where contact reflections have been used with people whose communication is distorted—perhaps as a way of using reflection to allow them time and space to try and express themselves more clearly—the effect is often very rapid emotional connections and engagement. Carers and nurses may find this difficult, especially if the sudden clarity of expression contains a request which the staff are unable to meet, such as asking to go home, find their mother or find a child that has died. This does not necessarily mean that the contact reflections are not useful but we may need to be prepared for rapid and often deep contact which has the potential to leave us with difficult raw emotions and feelings of helplessness and hopelessness in staff. We need to be aware that sometimes the raw emotional honesty of people with dementia can be quite profound for a worker who achieves empathic attunement. It is essential that staff are prepared for this eventuality, so that they can continue to work respectfully with those in their care, and simultaneously look after their own needs (Hansebo & Kihlgren, 2002; Innes, MacPherson & McCabe, 2006).

The need to be *doing* something

People with dementia frequently require high degrees of physical support from carers, relatives and support workers. In a simple example, we might be with a person who needs to get out of a chair. Clumsy continued contact reflections will almost certainly be counter-productive, leaving the person struggling to get up. Limited reflections would be best combined with the practical help they need. In dementia care we must not forget that there is a constant interplay of the physical with the psychological and at times reflections are not what is needed. Actual physical help and *doing* is required.

Contact reflections or Pre-Therapy?

We have seen in several chapters of this book the importance of the difference between contact work and Pre-Therapy. It is equally important in dementia care to consider the role in which you are working and how that determines whether you will be doing contact work or Pre-Therapy.

For support staff and carers, using contact reflections may be useful as a precursor to, facilitator of, or accompaniment to, physical care. For professional staff and nurses, the contact reflections may be used to try and enhance contact prior to using another therapeutic approach such as REMINISCENCE or activities-based approaches. Here contact work is more in line with the MILIEU therapy described by Dion Van Werde in Chapter 6 and on pages 18 and 19. This recognises that people who are not counsellors or psychotherapists might use contact work to facilitate other forms of work.

For people working in a counselling or psychotherapy role, the contact work may lead to further therapeutic work which aims at a more sustained engagement with the emotional world of the person with dementia. This specialised work requires skills in sustaining conversations with people with dementia which, due to the nature of the illness, are unlikely to be presented in coherent, logical patterns of speech. It also requires knowledge and skills in VALIDATION THERAPY or the ability to piece together disjointed narratives that the person with dementia presents (Feil, 1993; Goldsmith, 1996; Killick, 2005).

In summary, Pre-Therapy contact reflections hold the potential to contribute to the repertoire of both general support and skilled therapeutic communication with people with dementia. This way of working is relatively new in the field of dementia care but this brief introduction may provide people, whatever their role, with some ideas about how they might incorporate contact work into a field which is difficult, rewarding and relatively neglected, but holds vast potential to improve the quality of communication with and the daily lives of people with dementia.

8

PRE-THERAPY AND CONTACT WORK
FOR PEOPLE WITH LEARNING AND
OTHER MENTAL DISABILITIES

For people with a mental disability (such as learning disabilities, genetic deficiencies, congenital or developmental brain defects, etc.) Pre-Therapy can be helpful in *counselling* as well as in *everyday care*. However, in both areas, it is usually not a question of using 'pure' Pre-Therapy, but about *integrating pre-therapeutic elements into person-centred counselling or into person-centred everyday care*. Therefore, in this context, I prefer to talk about using 'pre-therapeutic approaches' (Pörtner, in press).

1. COUNSELLING

Many people with mental disabilities, in addition to their specific impairment, suffer from psychological disorders (such as depression, bipolar disorder, anxiety, compulsiveness, PSYCHOTIC episodes, post-traumatic syndrome, etc.), from emotional problems, or struggle with their life situation. Like anyone else in a similar situation, counselling or psychotherapy should be available for them. Yet, it is a regrettable fact that there are still only very few practitioners prepared to work in this field and who are familiar with its specific conditions and demands (Pörtner, 2002).

For clients with a mental disability it is rarely possible to explicitly talk about, and work on, their problems. However, there are two main purposes for counselling: to strengthen contact functions, and to develop a more congruent SELF-CONCEPT. These are the pre-conditions for any further change to become possible (Pörtner, 2003/2007: 213–41). Traditional diagnostic categories only partly apply, because it is often not clear whether a specific behaviour is a symptom of a psychological condition or due to mental impairment. The advantage of the person-centred approach is that it does not primarily focus on diagnostics, but on trying *to understand the client's subjective world.* Particularly with persons who are not able to communicate on a cognitive level and who express themselves in bizarre and hardly intelligible ways, empathic understanding is indispensable for getting access to their inner world. Prouty's term 'pre-expressive' (Prouty, 1994, 1998; Prouty, Van Werde & Pörtner, 2002, and pp. 24–6 this volume) is particularly helpful here as it allows a deeper understanding of apparently incoherent ways of behaviour and expression.

Contact reflections sometimes are the only way to reach a non-verbal or severely disabled person. The German psychologist Barbara Krietemeyer describes an outstanding example of how she developed contact with an extremely aggressive and auto-aggressive woman by for some weeks just patiently staying near her, at a safe distance, trying to 'feel into' what she might be feeling and experiencing and then, in time, by carefully reflecting her subtle non-verbal signals. (Krietemeyer & Prouty, 2003; Pörtner, 2000/2007: 106–12). Slowly, an amazing change process took place, which nobody would ever have believed this woman capable of.

Also with persons able to express themselves verbally, there are sequences or moments in counselling when the use of contact reflections is indicated. To intertwine contact reflections with 'regular' person-centred responses—according to the clients' actual contact level—enables the therapist to accurately follow their abrupt switching from one level to the other—which persons who suffer from various mental disabilities frequently do.

Illustrative example: *Catherine often fantasised about accidents, ambulances, doctors and hospitals. She said that she had been at the hospital that morning helping the doctors, or talked about something that had been done to her there. It took me a while to realise that, hidden behind these fantasies, there was the real memory of the traumatic experience of having been sterilised at fourteen. Scattered over many therapy sessions the memory emerged in tiny fragments. Catherine would then abruptly change the subject not coming back to it for some time.*

Only in this way and at this tempo, was it possible for her to slowly approach the painful memory.

This corresponds with what Dion Van Werde describes as *grey-zone functioning* (Prouty, Van Werde & Pörtner, 2002: 81–90, and pages 27–8 and Chapter 5 this volume), By carefully following clients through this blurred area between the pre-expressive and expressive level, where it is not quite clear if what they express is real or DELUSIONAL, the therapist helps to clarify it. Van Werde's concept refers to PSYCHOTIC patients, but is also extremely helpful for clients with mental disabilities. Catherine's 'fantasies' were located in the *grey-zone* in that they were fragments of a real memory and at the same time DELUSIONAL in how they were mingled with Catherine's actual life as if they were happening now. The example of Catherine (Pörtner, 1990) confirms Prouty's assumption that delusions are SYMBOLISATIONS of concrete experiences.

Restoring, developing and strengthening contact functions— as defined by Prouty on three levels: contact with reality, with oneself, with others—is crucial for persons with mental disabilities. Mostly their contact functions are impaired or not sufficiently developed, be it just on one or on all three levels. Often the most impaired is the clients' contact with themselves—emotionally as well as physically.

> **Illustrative example:** *When Alex first came to counselling, he was not able to say anything about himself. When I referred to his experiencing or his feelings he got totally confused, and his stereotypical answer was: 'Don't know'. To verbally reflect how he was sitting, tight-lipped, deeply withdrawn in his chair, would have risked making him feel that I was mocking him. Whereas reflecting his attitude with my own body got me in touch with how he seemed to feel. So I began to physically reflect his body posture and expressions, and continued for several sessions. After some time he began to ask, 'Do you think so?' or 'Should I?' when I tentatively tried to verbalise how he might feel. I then replied that I did not know how he felt, but would like, together with him, to find it out. With time, he answered with 'yes' or 'no', or 'just a little' to reflections like 'you look sad' or 'you seem quite happy today'. Gradually he got more and more in contact with his feelings and slowly discovered his own words to express them.*

However, counselling for people with a mental disability is not of much help if what they can develop during the sessions is not supported in daily life. Therefore, person-centred everyday care is at least as important, and sometimes even more effective than counselling. A detailed concrete description of how to work in a person-centred way in this field is described in detail in Pörtner, 2000/2007.

2. EVERYDAY CARE

Working in a person-centred way does not mean transforming everyday situations into counselling sessions. Yet, daily life in itself offers many opportunities to *counteract or at least not constantly confirm negative SELF-CONCEPTS* (like 'I am stupid', 'I can't do it', 'Other's know better than I what is good for me', etc.), and to *stimulate, develop and reinforce contact functions*.

There are two ways of integrating pre-therapeutic elements into person-centred care:
- *Offering life conditions that strengthen contact functions* instead of impairing them even more
- *Using contact reflections* when the situation is appropriate

Contact strengthening life conditions
It is an unfortunately widespread misunderstanding of normalisation to organise daily life for people with disabilities in a way considered 'normal' (whatever that means), not taking into account existing limitations. Normalisation and integration do *not* mean to make disabled persons equal by denying their being impaired, but *to respect them as equals* despite, and *with*, their impairments. It implies offering them every support they need to find the best ways to cope with their unique circumstances. It is worth, in this context, to think about the impact life conditions have on a person's contact functions.

Many people with mental disabilities are stressed by overloaded schedules of occupational, educational and leisure programmes. Carers do this with best intentions to do a good job—forgetting that, for this purpose, *less might be more.*

Considering if an activity or situation is more likely to strengthen or to weaken the contact functions is a useful guideline for organising daily life.

The 'contact-MILIEU' Dion Van Werde created for a psychiatric ward (Prouty, Van Werde & Pörtner, 2002; Chapter 6 and pp. 18–19 this volume) is exemplary and demonstrates how, in various areas of daily life (such as occupational and leisure programmes, interior decoration, physical exercises etc.), there are many opportunities to reinforce—or at least to not further impair—fragile contact functions. His concepts can easily be transferred and adapted to everyday care for people with mental disabilities.

The use of contact reflections

A crucial task in person-centred care is to be aware of, and to try to understand and adequately respond to, a person's feelings, experiencing and needs. Contact reflections make this possible also with persons who are non-verbal or express themselves in strange and rudimentary ways. For example, a carer will get more in touch with a woman who, whenever she can, lies on the floor, by sometimes lying near her for a moment, instead of constantly trying to have her sit in her chair.

Contact reflections facilitate communication between carers and clients as well as the clients' contact with reality and with themselves. Moreover they are also indicated whenever we wish to adequately respond to grey-zone functioning, to overcome critical situations, reduce tension and avoid escalations.

Strengthening contact

For example, on a walk, the carer might reflect: 'You walk very fast', 'You look at the ground', (Body Reflections); 'We are walking in the woods', 'The sun shines' (Situational Reflection). Or at the shower: 'You are shivering' (Body Reflection); 'The water feels nice and warm', (combined Body and Situational Reflection). Or: 'You are frowning', 'You smile' (Facial Reflections). Or, responding to a person's oral expression: 'Wwumm', 'Lala', 'Grrrr!' (Word-for-Word Reflections).

Grey-zone functioning (see Chapter 5 and p. 27, this volume)
In everyday care, responding to a person's grey-zone functioning does not mean working on, or trying to decipher, DELUSIONAL material (as it does in psychotherapy), but helping the person to restore reality contact, while at the same time recognising her subjective world. For example, reflecting: 'Catherine talks about what she sees at the hospital and we are all sitting together in the kitchen having breakfast'.

Critical situations
For example, a person who is hurting herself might stop doing so if carers use body reflections—whether verbally or by doing the same (of course, without seriously hurting themselves) and perhaps saying 'ouch'! It helps the person to become aware of what she is doing to herself. Self-mutilation, for contact-impaired persons, often represents a desperate attempt to establish *some kind* of contact. In this situation body reflections can help them get into a more differentiated contact with themselves. Situational reflections are useful to ease tension and avoid escalation, particularly in vicious circles which repeat again and again, by saying, for example: 'We are going round in circles', 'You say yes, I say no,' 'You yell at me', 'We are both annoyed', 'We are shouting at each other'.

Carers sometimes feel embarrassed at first, when using contact reflections, especially body reflections, but with time, they can find it extremely helpful for the persons concerned as well as for themselves (for more on this see Penny Dodds' Chapter 9). To see how strange behaviours diminish when being reflected is a reassuring experience which makes carers feel more relaxed and more competent in their work.

These are some brief descriptions of examples of possibilities for using pre-therapeutic approaches in person-centred counselling and care for people with mental disabilities. Readers with particular interests in these applications are directed to the more detailed descriptions to be found in the publications referred to in this chapter.

9

SOME CONSIDERATIONS ON LEARNING AND TEACHING PRE-THERAPY CONTACT REFLECTIONS

THE PROCESS OF LEARNING CONTACT REFLECTIONS

As this book goes to press there are no official curricula in Pre-Therapy, and there are no qualifications in Pre-Therapy. Acknowledged Pre-Therapy trainers deliver tailor-made lectures, workshops, in-service training and short courses. There is only one published writing explicitly devoted to the supervision of Pre-Therapy (Prouty & Van Werde, in press).

It is an interesting question whether or not it is feasible for people who do not have a background in counselling or psychotherapy to learn and use Pre-Therapy, but this has not hitherto been addressed. For example, it would be restrictive to require people to have a qualification or accreditation in person-centred therapy in order to use the Pre-Therapy contact reflections. Any such restriction would limit the potential usefulness of the contact reflections for other professions, workers in other fields and relatives and carers.

If we offer non-therapists the chance to learn and use Pre-Therapy we must acknowledge different levels of ability, and opportunity, to work in a person-centred way. However, because Pre-Therapy is grounded in the person-centred approach, there needs to be some understanding of the principles of working in a person-centred way since simple mechanical replication of the contact reflections is certainly not sufficient, and may even be harmful since this could be experienced as too intrusive.

So we are faced with a dilemma—do we limit Pre-Therapy to the psychotherapists or do we encourage others to learn about Pre-Therapy and adopt it into their practice?

An important step is to differentiate between Pre-Therapy and contact work using contact reflections. Readers will have seen throughout this book that a range of psychological therapists use

Pre-Therapy as part of their therapeutic work with a client. Others, who are not therapists, draw on the principles of Pre-Therapy and use contact reflections as part of their own repertoire of therapeutic communication and interpersonal skills in whatever their role and client group they are working with. This is not done out of professional protectionism, rather it recognises the purpose and therapeutic goal of using Pre-Therapy and the respective professional focus of people with different roles.

Now we must consider how much 'training' is required for each role how can this be assessed, and how can we identify levels of competence for something which is so embedded in the artistry of *being* from a person-centred philosophical position. Furthermore there is a tension between seeing that contact reflections *require* grounding in person-centred philosophy, whilst understanding that basic level training and education cannot simply *teach* people to be person-centred (for more on this see Sanders, 2006). The Pre-Therapy International Network is currently exploring this issue and residential institutions in Belgium that have integrated Pre-Therapy and contact work into their daily care are looking at the teaching of Pre-Therapy (developments will be occasionally posted on <www.pre-therapy.com>).

This chapter looks at issues that have arisen for qualified nurses, student nurses and support workers in mental health settings. It takes a closer look at the learning process and their experiences. This goes some way in exploring what happens when staff who are not qualified counsellors or psychotherapists are introduced to Pre-Therapy.

My ideas for this chapter come from two sources. Firstly, my doctoral research (in the field of dementia care) exploring the learning and using of contact reflections by people who are not psychotherapists. Secondly, the chapter draws on experiences of pre-registration mental health student nurses who work in a variety of mental health settings with different client groups as part of their training. All staff received an introductory workshop or teaching session on Pre-Therapy and contact reflections. The participants in the research project received follow-up meetings offering supervision and asking for feedback about their experience of implementing the contact work and their own experiences. The feedback from the mental health student nurses was more informal; mainly gathering experiences from those who had tried to take contact reflections into their own practice.

Experience tells us that the relationship between teaching and learning is not straightforward. Learning is a process, and some of the experiences of going through the journey of learning contact reflections indicate that learning contact reflections is not as straightforward as it appears. I have included these because I think they may have relevance if you are either in the position of learning and using contact reflections, or if you are in the position of 'teaching' others.

TEACHING CONTACT REFLECTIONS TO OTHERS

Below I present the contents of a very basic introduction to Pre-Therapy which has been given to staff as part of my doctoral project over a single session which might vary between one hour and three hours.

Content of an initial workshop
Basic introduction to Pre-Therapy contact reflections
- Basic principles of person-centred philosophy: how we are with people
- Development of Prouty's Pre-Therapy: the theoretical origins
- Noticing: focusing on the concrete lived experience of the world of the client
- The pre-expressive and expressive self, and grey-zone functioning
- The contact functions
- The contact reflections
- The contact behaviours
- Identify the difference between contact reflections and other ways of interacting

The teaching process of the introductory session includes didactic teaching of theoretical concepts; experiential exercises allowing people to role play using contact reflections; small group work; and group discussion of how staff might imagine the use of contact reflections in their own practice.

Immediately obvious but not as simple as it sounds

A common response of staff after an initial workshop is that the contact reflections seem obvious and have a high relevance to staff who work with people with a mental health disturbance. Perhaps, not surprisingly, the relevance is seen most by nursing staff who are working in in-patient settings with people who are experiencing a severe level of disturbance and distress.

However, very quickly, many people find that whilst the contact reflections seem straightforward on paper, they are much more difficult to do than they seem. It would appear that concreteness of the contact reflections is both a strength and a difficulty for staff. A strength is that the contact reflections reveal to staff, through their own observations, precisely what they are doing—they are reflecting what they see and notice in their own behaviour. Difficulties arise firstly when people begin to see that there are minute but complex decisions to be made in offering contact reflections and secondly when their underestimation of the complexities and subtleties of offering contact reflections becomes apparent. These are summarised below.

Deciding which contact reflection to offer

The worker has to gauge the situation and choose which type of reflection appears to be the most appropriate.

Gauging the level of expressiveness

The worker has to make a judgement about whether a person is in a pre-expressive state, in grey-zone functioning or is expressive.

Gauging the delivery of the contact reflection

This may involve deciding whether to enhance a contact reflection with a stronger non-verbal gesture which adds depth to the reflection. For example simply stating that the window is open (situational reflections) or whether to accompany the verbal situational reflection with a gesture such as pointing to the window.

Using themselves in the delivery of the contact reflections
This involves adopting a position of offering warmth, acceptance, regard and an empathic presence on the part of the worker. It may be seen in the tone, pitch and pace of the delivery of a contact reflection.

The knowledge required
These complexities are related to the need for some underlying knowledge about the theory of Pre-Therapy. Arguably any training or education program will need to address this foundation knowledge, since in many ways it is crucial to being able to use contact reflections with confidence in different circumstances as they affect individual patients or clients. Understanding of the concept of the pre-expressive self is central to this. For more on the pre-expressive self, see pages 25–7 and Prouty (1998).

Frequently workers can identify people who fit the description of someone who is pre-expressive and this helps them begin to identify the differences between the pre-expressive and the expressive self. In relation to mental health nursing, the main problems appear to come from gauging the level of expressiveness when a person is fluctuating between expressive, pre-expressive and grey-zone functioning. This has led to nurses feeling hesitant about whether to offer a contact reflection or another type of interaction such as a question.

Secondly, and just as important, is the need for knowledge about the core principles of the person-centred approach as a way of being. This is essential to avoid contact reflections being seen, and applied, as a mechanical technique; something that you simply do, or apply, *to* a person, rather than contact reflections being what you *do*; supported from the very foundation of *how you are* with a person.

The third area of essential knowledge is having an appropriate level of self-understanding and an ability to reflect or consider how you as a worker and a person conduct yourself in helping relationships. Whilst critical self reflection is built into nurse training, some unqualified nurses are not used to self-reflection on their own practice and this is likely to be a problem in the effective use of Pre-Therapy and contact work.

Feeling awkward vs. feeling natural

The experiences of staff in the early stages of learning and using contact reflections fall roughly into two categories—'feeling awkward' and 'feeling natural'. For some staff the use of contact reflections feels strange and unnatural. It seems that, for them, offering a concrete contact reflection somehow challenges the normal rules of social conversation. As a rule, normal social interaction is based on the assumption that two people are both in an expressive state. Where workers hold this reasonable assumption of expressiveness they are more likely to find the contact reflections awkward since using contact reflections challenges the workers' internalised rules of social conversation. Therefore a worker may approach a person who is pre-expressive with PSYCHOTIC experiences with an opening conversation that does not recognise the pre-expressive state of the person, for example 'Hello Tom, have you been out yet, it looks quite cold'. In contrast, where the worker recognises the pre-expressive state, the worker may offer a concrete reflection 'Tom is standing by the door'. As fragments of social interaction, they are quite different, and as an opening gambit in an interaction, they shape the rest of the relationship episode considerably. This leads staff to reconsider the extent to which their interactions with a client are focused on, and led by, the person. By their very nature, contact reflections mean that it is the world of the client that is determining the direction of an interaction.

Overcoming awkwardness

Some staff were less inclined to find the contact reflections awkward. Much of this seemed to stem from having better understood the principles behind the pre-expressive self, expressive self and grey-zone functioning. In addition they may have natural tendencies towards feeling more comfortable with interactions which do not follow traditional rules of conversation, but rather follow a therapeutic goal. Furthermore, it may be that the greater the level of empathic contact with a client, the more 'natural' a contact reflection feels, as the worker is drawing on the principles of adopting a client-focused approach and is skilled in noticing and focusing on the experiences of the client. In Martin Buber's (1958) terminology, the greater the person's capacity for I–Thou relating, the more comfortable they might be with offering a contact reflection.

The discomfort of unknowing
Alongside initial levels of awkwardness, some workers also experience discomfort in the process of un-knowing and un-learning that occurs. In an ideal world all learning is progressive and is supported in practice. So where possible, supported learning is preferable; however the reality of much 'training' is that people are simply given a training session then left to implement it—the session is disconnected from the actual work. Where this occurs we are much more likely to see the ideas not translating to practice.

Responses to contact work
A common theme reported by staff is that contact reflections have produced reactions or responses in *themselves* which have surprised them. Nurses have described feeling 'very in tune' with the client or patient, or achieving a depth of emotional engagement with them that somehow felt 'out of the ordinary'. There have been times when nurses felt that they were 'seeing inside the person' which felt different from their usual experience of patient interactions. Whilst it may indicate that a depth of understanding between the client/patient and the nurse has been achieved and the contact reflections have somehow helped facilitate a person from a pre-expressive state to an expressive state, this experience is not always comfortable for nurses or people who may not have the experience or training in managing their own emotional states.

The movement of a relationship towards engagement based on an empathic understanding of the subjective world of the other can prove very emotionally challenging for those in a role which does not have the ethos of counselling and psychotherapy. The workers in such roles may simply be unprepared for the level of personal and emotional material which surfaces. In particular, working with people with dementia, staff have found the rapid nature of getting emotional contact has led to them feeling overwhelmed by the emotions of the person with dementia. This may have something to do with the nature of the dementing illness, since there is no record of similar reports where people use contact reflections with a client/patient with PSYCHOSIS.

The can of worms
In addition, and related to the discomfort experienced by nurses of seeing the *person,* is the worry that the contact reflections will open a can of worms. This phrase is repeatedly mentioned by people attending initial workshops. This worry appears to be well-founded, at least in one area, since the can of worms has been experienced by staff working with dementia. Again this may be related to the nature of dementing illnesses, because people with dementia frequently carry painful emotions and memories close to the surface and the lightest contact with them gives these difficult emotions the space to be aired. From my own experience of introducing contact work to nurses working in dementia care, I now advise them to be aware of the consequences of getting contact. This involves spending more time preparing people for the personal implications of contact.

The effect of their role concept
This can of worms also seems to be related to the 'role concept' that a worker has internalised. In the same way staff hold internalised rules of social conversation, they also carry an internalised role concept. Some of the discomfort associated with contact reflections seems to arise where using a Pre-Therapy approach contradicts their self and/or role concept. This is particularly evident where nurses feel that their role is to soothe and comfort—seeing themselves as someone who 'makes it better'. As a result, some staff shy away from engaging with painful emotions and feel reluctant to use contact

reflections which may well invite and encourage the expression of such difficult emotions. In contrast, where nurses understand their role to be to 'witness and stand by' the pain of another, 'work with the experience of another' or 'engage with the bad feelings as well as the good', they find it more comfortable to sustain an emotional engagement with the client.

Autonomy
In terms of roles, there is a big difference between the daily work of a nurse and the role of a counsellor. Nurses working on in-patient units arguably have less autonomy and control over their work. They are sometimes at the mercy of the environment as much as the clients/patients. Telephones ring, people call for help, relatives visit and they have less opportunity for boundaried work (in terms of time and private space). In addition they are working in an environment where they have responsibility for a group of clients or patients rather than working solely on a one-to-one basis.

These differences require careful consideration when it comes to understanding how contact reflections may be compatible, or otherwise, with the work demands of staff within their particular work setting. It is most common for staff to believe that they haven't got the time to integrate contact work into their routine. Whilst acknowledging the pressures that busy health care and psychological therapies staff are under, such a response may indicate that they do not appreciate the extent to which the use of contact interventions might improve the appropriateness and efficiency of their interpersonal communications and actually save time. Where staff have time to say 'hello Tom, have you been out yet, it looks quite cold', they almost certainly have the time to offer a contact reflection instead. Having said that, they might not have the time to follow up and work with the consequences of *real* interactions with patients rather than the frequently brief and instrumental routine *conversations* so often based on everyday pleasantries and tasks rather than emotional content.

One of the most useful things for staff is to begin to integrate contact work into the work that they are doing. In this way contact work becomes part of the repertoire of skills that a nurse can draw on and, hopefully, soon be used with a light touch. This confirms what we might have assumed to be obvious, namely that the focus of contact work for nurses is different from that of a psychotherapist. Pre-Therapy contact reflections will probably be used by a therapist to help the client to a point where they can use the relationship for therapy. For nurses, the contact work might be a way of getting contact prior to collaborating with a client on something more practical or tangible, managing medications, dressing or meal times, etc. This reflects very much the work of Dion Van Werde where nurses use contact work to help anchor the patient in reality by using the contact reflections when the patient is in grey-zone functioning, to help maintain the patient in an expressive state (for more on this see Chapter 5). In this way the nurse is weaving contact reflections into their communication with the patient to strengthen their level of expressiveness and limit their withdrawal into pre-expressive states.

There are other practical applications of contact work for nurses when a person is more clearly in a pre-expressive state. More commonly this is seen by staff as using contact work because other overtures and attempts at conversation are failing to make any contact or relationship with the patient.

The example below illustrates the use of contact work by a mental health student nurse who was assessing a client in the Accident and Emergency psychiatric liaison department.

> **Illustrative example:** *Mrs A was suffering a severe depressive episode which was accompanied by fixed ideas that she was being poisoned. As a result she had neither eaten nor drunk and was in danger of dehydration. A mental health assessment was proving difficult as Mrs A was detached, not responding to questions and appeared to be pre-expressive. The student nurse, Carl, decided to try and use contact reflections as a way of engaging with Mrs A to see if this would help him begin a dialogue with her, so that an assessment of her mental state could be made. Carl informed his mentor (a registered mental health nurse) that he wanted to try out using contact reflections. Carl did indeed manage to gradually engage with Mrs A to the point that*

she answered limited questions and could sustain a conversation for short periods of time. Carl was sufficiently sensitive to be able to gauge when to move from reflecting to asking questions, and he saw that her level of expressiveness would ebb and flow. By following this ebbing and flowing of her level of expressiveness he was able to switch back to contact reflections when necessary.

Contact reflections in context

It is also important to consider the context in which contact work takes place in order better to understand how this might affect staff who have received initial introduction to Pre-Therapy and want to use it in their practice. It is in the nature of nursing work, that its interactions are frequently in public and shared spaces. Whilst individuals may have their own rooms there is a likelihood that staff will need to be prepared to do contact work in front of others. The following personal and contextual factors may affect an individual's capacity to use contact work in such shared and public spaces.

Personal factors:
1. Self-consciousness: because the contact reflections are not usual conversations, staff may feel self-conscious about how they appear to others.
2. Fear of a difficult response that is on public view: staff have expressed concern that the contact reflections may elicit a response from the client that *goes wrong* and that this will further expose the nurse in front of colleagues.
3. Fear that the contact reflections may look like they are mimicking or parodying the client.

Contextual factors:
1. Lack of awareness amongst colleagues about contact reflections—all of the personal factors are exacerbated when a member of staff uses contact reflections in the presence of colleagues who are not familiar with them. This leads to the nurse using the contact reflections being concerned that other

staff may question or disapprove of what they are doing.
2. Subtle sabotage by other staff who question or do not understand what the nurse is doing. Because of the nature of nurses working in groups, the micro-culture of the ward can be very powerful. The ward culture creates group norms. If contact work is not part of the ward culture, the dominant group can sabotage a worker who is trying something new.
3. The mechanism of group conformity and maintaining their social identity by conforming to group norms means that the nurse may give up using contact reflections.

A way of overcoming these contextual factors is to introduce a whole unit or ward to contact work so that there is a common understanding of contact work. In this way contact work becomes part of the therapeutic MILIEU and is more likely to be adopted as part of the work of the unit. There are practical difficulties which need to be overcome for this to happen such as frequent turnover of staff and the difficulties in arranging teaching time for all staff. This way of working is looked at in detail in Chapter 6.

CONCLUSION

The introduction of Pre-Therapy to nursing staff brings mixed results. Careful preparation of all staff and commitment to the Pre-Therapy/contact work methodology are essential. For some staff a short introduction may be sufficient for them to start using contact work. For others a short introduction is not sufficient because of the factors discussed in this chapter. The following should be considered when introducing contact work to others in healthcare settings:
1. The nature of the client/patient group and their particular needs
2. The level of natural and intuitive empathy of staff
3. The ability to understand the basic concepts of the person-centred approach and the theoretical foundations of Pre-Therapy
4. Appropriate preparation of staff for the emotional response they may experience when they achieve contact

5. Carefully considering the level of knowledge that staff will need
6. Identifying how contact work fits with their existing roles and work settings
7. The introduction of contact work to a whole team to enable it to become part of the culture of their work
8. Thinking through and planning how the teaching can be followed up by support and reflection on practice

An ongoing process of facilitated learning is preferable to short one-off didactic teaching. It is possible that the process of learning contact reflections will help staff become more person-centred in the long run, as the process of learning to use contact reflections requires sensitivity to the world of the other; used with an *attitude* that is aligned to their world. Some nurses undergoing basic contact work training have described how it changed their perception of the client or patient, giving them a deeper sense of seeing the person within.

By exploring and reflecting on what happens when people learn and use contact reflections we get nearer to understanding some of the complexities that people encounter. So far it has clearly shown that there is significant potential for contact work to be incorporated into the day-to-day working practice of a range of healthcare workers and professionals with a wide range of different roles with clients.

10

RESEARCH INTO PRE-THERAPY[1]

In many books on counselling and psychotherapy it is taken as read that the only research question anyone is interested in is 'Does it work?' Whilst this *is* a question which will concern many readers, there are a few issues which need to be looked at first.

A couple of these issues have been covered in *The Person-Centred Counselling Primer* (pp. 103–4), and I repeat them (slightly amended) here in the next five paragraphs.

In many places in our culture, research in psychology is presented as scientific. From its early days in the nineteenth century, psychologists thought that psychology's best chance of gaining credibility was to separate itself from philosophy and become more like the physical sciences. So they set about measuring things and counting things just like physicists and biologists, etc. Quite naturally this led to thinking that human beings not only were 'living machines' but that human mental life, 'the mind' was amenable to counting, measurement, and machine metaphors.

It pretty soon became clear that counting and measurement, when applied to the mind and human experience, was incredibly difficult and the results were highly variable—in fact hardly any two scientific psychologists could get the same measurements on anything. If the truth is revealed by scientific analysis, then quantifying the mind and human experience was proving difficult.

Two innovations proved interesting. One was the physical/natural sciences method of dividing the things you are looking at into smaller and smaller units until you were at a level where things actually *did* provide RELIABLE measurements. This is called REDUCTIONISM. The second was to insist that scientific psychology

---

1. I am grateful to Mathias Dekeyser for his generous feedback and advice on late drafts of this chapter.

should stick to the observable and measurable events in human life, i.e. behaviour. Descriptions of experiences, feelings and such like were not admissible. This was the basis of BEHAVIOURISM.

There were problems with REDUCTIONISM and BEHAVIOURISM. After a while people (even psychologists) thought that the research was demeaning (they didn't like being thought of as, and treated like, machines) and ridiculous (some research involved measuring extremely esoteric factors far removed from human everyday experience). This gave rise to HUMANISTIC PSYCHOLOGY which in turn revived interest in researching the *qualities* of human experience rather than the *quantities* of human behaviour (hence the terms QUALITATIVE and QUANTITATIVE research).

Person-centred psychology finds itself better suited to QUALITATIVE research, but it is not so simple for Pre-Therapy and contact work. The problem is that since Pre-Therapy is associated with chronic human conditions which mostly fall into the category of psychiatric or medical conditions, medical-style research which looks at interventions like Pre-Therapy as a 'cure' for an 'illness' or a 'fix' for something 'broken', is seen as the only sort of useful study. Therefore RANDOMISED CONTROLLED TRIALS (RCTs: a QUANTITATIVE method) are required in the UK by NICE (National Institute for Health and Clinical Excellence) in order to sanction a 'treatment'.

This sort of study is seen as essential, to the extent that it is sometimes called the 'gold standard' of research evidence. However, there are problems with such studies:

1. RCTs are very expensive: requiring careful planning, access to large numbers of very specifically diagnosed client groups, complex ethical clearance and provision of carefully constructed treatments and controls.

2. Funding is difficult to obtain. Psychological therapies research funding is a classic 'catch-22'. In order to obtain the high levels of funding necessary, therapies need to demonstrate that they are worth investigating (next to many other competing therapies), but without evidence of some sort, the funding for the research is next-to-impossible to obtain …

3. RCT methodology is modelled on the scientific method

designed to test drugs. This is fine for treatments that can be given in measured doses, but psychotherapy and interpersonal relationship-based methods like Pre-Therapy can hardly be given in 'doses' and 'measured' without the possibility of distorting them to the point of INVALIDITY.

4. RCTs hinge on, amongst other things, the quality of the design. In particular, is the way the treatment and control groups are constructed. Are these groups truly equivalent? Sometimes control and/or treatment group practitioners are only trained in the treatment method for a few hours. Also, more experienced practitioners normally have a strong allegiance to their preferred approach, in comparison with 'controls'. This reasonable (but biased) therapist enthusiasm and allegiance to their approach contributes significantly to outcome results regardless of approach.

Even so, such methods are required if NICE or any funding organisation is going to recommend or otherwise sanction a 'treatment'. Pre-Therapy, along with other therapeutic approaches and techniques, has little or no evidence to support it from empirical studies and RCTs because only one Pre-Therapy study to date (Hinterkopf, Prouty & Brunswick, 1979) comes close to RCT methodology. Funding the research is a major stumbling block. However, academics in Europe and America have conducted a range of research studies limited to single cases or very small SAMPLES.

RESEARCH INTO PRE-THERAPY

In his review of HUMANISTIC psychotherapy for people with SCHIZOPHRENIA in Cain and Seeman (2001), Garry Prouty included some SINGLE-CASE-STUDIES and other small-scale research on Pre-Therapy. What research there is on Pre-Therapy reveals some interesting questions which we will look at below. Since there is so little research on the subject it is difficult to say, at this stage, whether we are any nearer answering the questions. Readers will likely be frustrated to learn, as explained above, that there is hardly any research on the effectiveness of Pre-Therapy.

What does the research tell us about Pre-Therapy theory?
Pre-Therapy is pan-theoretical in both its application and appeal, lending itself to explanation from many different therapeutic viewpoints. Put bluntly, does the research tell us anything about how Pre-Therapy affects people? For example, does it:
  • Increase psychological contact?
    This is the person/client-centred theory position, from where Prouty started in his own thinking.
  • Develop appropriate interpersonal and social behaviour?
    It could be that any changes in behaviour as a result of contact reflections are due to a learning or developmental process which results in more appropriate relationship behaviour (which would, of course, include sensing and communicating aspects of the internal and external world of the client).
  • Improve meaning-related linguistic ability?
    Since this ability has been studied in the fields of aging and schizophrenia, we might speculate that contact reflections may distinctly affect this ability.

Dekeyser, Prouty and Elliott (in press) suggest that all three are plausible, and since Pre-Therapy methods are accepted by a wide variety of practitioners, it may be that the effects of contact reflections will indeed eventually be explained in many ways from different theoretical perspectives.

Another, related question is, what is contact behaviour evidence of? In strictly behavioural terms it is difficult to measure LATENT contact, or awareness of the world, without attendant communication. Dekeyser, Prouty and Elliott (in press) argue that contact behaviour equals meaningful communication, i.e., that in principle, all measures of the meaningfulness of communication can be used as measures of contact behaviour. All of the detectable indicators of contact must be based on the ability to communicate effectively, which assumes, of course, that the communication is in context.

Can contact behaviours be measured?
In the preceding section we asked what a list of agreed contact

behaviours might look like. If any meaningful communication can be considered to be evidence of contact, the effort to identify an 'agreed' set of behavioural indicators is made easier. Nevertheless if contact behaviours are the signals that tell us whether or not psychological contact is established, it is important to have reliable methods for measuring them. Such measures would be useful for research and, hopefully, to therapists and carers to help estimate the level of functioning of their patients and clients. When reviewing efforts to measure contact behaviours, readers must remember that, as explained in the previous section, *communication* is implicit in all contact behaviour.

Measuring contact behaviour is complicated because some clients may be non-verbal or effectively mute, others have speech production problems, disorganised speech, and so on. In addition, a client's level of communication can change during Pre-Therapy. Most measures are applicable only to certain types of communication difficulty—it is no good trying to measure meaning-related linguistic ability if the client is mute. They may nevertheless be able to communicate with some degree of effectiveness.

On this basis Hinterkopf, Prouty and Brunswick (1979) produced the Pre-Therapy Rating Scale (PTRS), in which client responses to semi-structured interview questions are rated for contact indicators such as: communication of basic reality; emotive words; emotive words with corresponding AFFECT, and conversely, *failure* to communicate reality and AFFECT. The procedure is made more objective by training independent raters to rate the responses.

Prouty revised the PTRS in 1990 by, for example, changing the contact indicators to reality, affect, social communication, and PSYCHOTIC communication. One drawback of the second version (PTRS-2) is that the 'PSYCHOTIC communication' scale, overemphasises the application of Pre-Therapy to clients with a diagnosis of PSYCHOSIS. This second version of the scale shows very high inter-rater reliability, indicating that it might be a useful starting point for a research tool measuring changes in contact behaviour before and after Pre-Therapy.

Sandwiched in between these developments of the PTRS is the work of Dinacci (1997) who developed the Evaluation Criterion for the Pre-Therapy Interview for more verbally disorganised clients (in contrast to the more verbally-oriented PTRS).

Does Pre-Therapy work?

Dekeyser, Prouty and Elliott (in press) summarise the findings of the few available Pre-Therapy outcome studies (including Hinterkopf et al., 1979; Dinacci, 1997; Prouty & Cronwall, 1990). These studies involved a restricted range of clients with chronic conditions diagnosed as SCHIZOPHRENIA and mental handicap. In other words, the most severely withdrawn people with challenging communication difficulties.

Hinterkopf et al. (1979) paired fourteen chronic SCHIZOPHRENIC patients, hospitalised on average for 20 years on the basis of PTRS scores (making seven pairs with similar scores). Patients from each pair were randomly allocated to the treatment and the control group. The patients in the treatment group received one hour of Pre-Therapy per week and the control group received recreational therapy. The PTRS was administered again after six months to detect any improvement. Although it was reported that a higher number of patients in treatment group showed improvements, the differences have been shown to be not STATISTICALLY SIGNIFICANT.

The remaining research is characterised by relying on small samples and none complies with the requirements of RCT studies. Although none of the studies show STATISTICALLY SIGNIFICANT results, they show *consistent and, in some cases, sizeable improvements* in functioning.

Although without RCT methodology most observers would find the research 'interesting' at best, as small-scale outcome studies accumulate positive findings, it is possible to construct an argument based on the META-ANALYSIS of many such studies. Unfortunately, Pre-Therapy research is not yet at a stage which generates enough data for an incisive META-ANALYSIS, but Dekeyser et al. (in press) make a noteworthy effort by surveying all studies to date. Readers with an interest in research are invited to (a) read the studies mentioned and Prouty's recent work which includes research reviews (Prouty, 2001), and (b) support Pre-Therapy research opportunities whenever and wherever they arise.

11

THE FUTURE FOR
PRE-THERAPY AND CONTACT WORK

I highlight this development in the Person-Centered Approach [Pre-Therapy] because it is the one area which has the potential to make a profound impact on much of psychiatric practice. (Freeth, 2007: 149)

The practice of Pre-Therapy and the use of contact reflections in a range of settings is now well established in several institutions in European countries. The St Camillus psychiatric hospital, Gent, Belgium is the best example of the contact MILIEU in action, with the treatment ward for people suffering PSYCHOSIS devoted to the principles of contact work (indeed where the whole idea was developed) and the principal psychologist and staff jointly use Pre-Therapy as a therapeutic approach. A selection of projects includes:

Acute psychiatry and crisis intervention Pre-Therapy has been introduced into the psychiatric crisis intervention and emergency wards, and the day-care programme at the ZOL general hospital in Genk, Belgium.

Chronic psychiatry The St Amandus psychiatric hospital, Beernem, Belgium, integrates Pre-Therapy in individual therapy by psychologists and in group sessions for chronic PSYCHOTIC and/or patients with mental disabilities.

At the Sans Souci hospital in Brussels, the staff on two wards received in-service training in Pre-Therapy. As a consequence of the influence of the training, staff were also invited to give suggestions on how to integrate the concepts of contact into the architecture of a new pavillion.

Pre-Therapy has also been introduced in St Amadeus hospital in Mortsel and in the psychiatric centre Bethanië in Zoersel, Belgium.

Special needs, learning and other mental disabilities Two organisations responsible for the care of people with various mental disabilities work systematically (including quality management) with the contact-work and person-centred concepts introduced by Marlis Pörtner in her book *Trust and Understanding*. These are: 'Stiftung für Schwerbehinderte Luzern' (SSBL) (Pörtner, 2002/2007: 76), Lucerne, Switzerland and 'Arbeiter-Samariter-Bund' (ASB) (Pörtner, 2002/2007: 75) Bremen, Germany.

Gerontopsychiatry Person-centred therapy and Pre-Therapy are core ingredients of the treatment philosophy on several wards in the St Norbertshuis psychiatric hospital, Duffel, Belgium.

Czech Republic The organisation 'Quality in Practice' received European Union funding to provide Pre-Therapy training—including the work of Marlis Pörtner, detailed in Pörtner (2002/2007)—for representatives from a diverse range of institutions on care for a variety of mentally challenged people. The clients (many in institutional care) include severely contact-impaired people due to multiple diagnosis, and dementing elderly people with behavioural problems.

Mental health nurse training Pre-Therapy is part of the curriculum of the Mental Health Branch programme of nurse training at the University of Paisley in Scotland. Pre-Therapy contributes to the section covering the needs of clients experiencing PSYCHOSIS from a SCHIZOPHRENIC perspective and severe and enduring mental illnesses. The School of Nursing and Midwifery will, from August 2007, be the largest in Scotland; responsible for training several cohorts of mental health nurses each year.

Inspirational cases Cases are presented at the Pre-Therapy International Network annual meeting. Bea Conickx (Belgium) reported that a patient in a severely regressed silence for 35 years had been restored sufficiently to engage in long-term psychotherapy. Dr Elenia Poli (Italy), illustrated her work—with video recordings— with a patient with an irreversible neurological condition, mute and regressed for 50 years. After six years of weekly Pre-Therapy sessions he gradually resumed speaking and more normal social contact.

APPENDIX
RESOURCES FOR LEARNING

ORGANISATIONS

• Pre-Therapy International Network <www.pre-therapy.com>
• World Association for Person-Centered and Experiential Psychotherapy and Counseling (WAPCEPC) <www.pce-world.org>
• British Association for the Person-Centred Approach (BAPCA) <www.bapca.org.uk>

JOURNALS

Apart from an informal journal (*International Pre-Therapy Review*) with a very limited circulation, edited by Aldo Dinacci, there are no journals dedicated to Pre-Therapy and contact work. However, papers on Pre-Therapy, contact work and associated ideas are regularly published in *Person-Centered and Experiential Psychotherapies,* the quarterly journal of WAPCEPC (also sent to the members of several European person-centred associations as part of their subscription).

WEBSITES

• The Pre-Therapy International Network website has the most recent developments in Pre-Therapy worldwide: <www.pre-therapy.com>
• Another web resource for Pre-Therapy is the site run by Catherine Clarke. It contains a bibliography: <http://www.psychological-wellbeing.co.uk>

Since websites occasionally change their URL or simply disappear, a good, up-to-date list of links can be found at: <www.pccs-books.co.uk/page.php?xPage=links.html>

FURTHER READING

Since much Pre-Therapy literature has been published in mainland Europe, little of the detailed work on applications is available in English. However, there are still dozens of books and articles which may be of interest to you (see the references section of this book), depending on your level of study and aspirations. If you feel overwhelmed by the sheer amount available, these are the articles and books that the contributors to this book think are particularly useful and/or important. We have chosen writings that are up-to-date, in print and available in the UK. It is *not* a definitive list.

More advanced *general* grounding in Pre-Therapy theory and practice
Prouty, G, Van Werde, D & Pörtner, M (2002) *Pre-Therapy: Reaching contact-impaired clients.* Ross-on-Wye: PCCS Books. Original German edition (1998) *Prä-Therapie.* Stuttgart: Klett-Cotta.

The most advanced Pre-Therapy theory and practice
Prouty, GF (ed) (in press) *Emergent Developments in Pre-Therapy.* Ross-on-Wye: PCCS Books.

For particular applications of Pre-Therapy and contact work
In this mixed section of writings some books contain one or more chapters describing applications, some are entirely devoted to this way of working.

Coffeng, T (2002) Contact in the therapy of trauma and dissociation. In G Wyatt & P Sanders (eds) *Rogers' Therapeutic Conditions, Volume 4: Contact and Perception* (pp. 153–67). Ross-on-Wye: PCCS Books.
Dekeyser, M, Prouty, GF & Elliott, R (in press) Pre-Therapy process and outcome: A review of research instruments and results. *Person-Centered and Experiential Psychotherapies.*
Dodds P, Morton I, Prouty G (2004) Using Pre-Therapy techniques in dementia care. *Journal of Dementia Care 12,* 2, 25–8.
*Krietemeyer, B & Prouty, G (2003) The art of psychological contact: The psychotherapy of a retarded psychotic client. In *Person-Centered & Experiential Psychotherapies, 2,* 3, 151–61.
Pörtner, M (2007) *Trust and Understanding· The person-centered approach in everyday care for people with special needs.* Second, revised and extended edition. Ross-on-Wye: PCCS Books.
Sommerbeck, L (2003) *The Client-Centred Therapist in Psychiatric Contexts: A therapists' guide to the psychiatric landscape and its inhabitants.* Ross-on-Wye: PCCS Books.
*Van Werde, D (2002) The falling man: Pre-Therapy applied to somatic hallucinating. *Person-Centred Practice 10,* 2, 101–7.
Van Werde, D (2005) Facing psychotic functioning: Person-centred contact work in residential psychiatric care. In S Joseph & R Worsley, (eds) *Person-Centred Psychopathology: A positive psychology of mental health* (pp. 158–68). Ross-on-Wye: PCCS Books.
Van Werde, D & Morton, I (1999) The relevance of Prouty's Pre-Therapy to dementia care. In I Morton (ed) *Person-Centred Approaches to Dementia Care* (pp. 139–66). Bicester: Winslow Press.

* Reproduced (slightly amended) in R Worsley & S Joseph (eds) (2007) *Person-Centred Practice: Case studies in positive psychology.* Ross-on-Wye: PCCS Books.

GLOSSARY

ACUPHASE   Abbreviated name for Clopixol Acuphase, a NEUROLEPTIC drug.

ADAPTATION   A biological term: a change due to natural selection over a period of time to a feature (structural, physiological or behavioural) of an organism.

AFFECT   In psychology used to mean emotion or feeling state. 'AFFECTIVE' roughly means 'emotional'.

AKATHESIA   Restlessness as a result of NEUROLEPTIC medication. Stereotypical movement patterns such as pacing, body rocking, or foot tapping.

ALIENATION   Estrangement or separation; intrapersonally (one part of personality from another), interpersonally (from family), social (from society).

AUTISTIC   Usually refers to *autism*; a pervasive developmental disorder, but here used to include more general severe and chronic communicative difficulties and withdrawal without a specific diagnosis of autism.

BEHAVIOURISM   A 'school' of objective psychology and philosophy which rejects subjective experience and consciousness. It states that the only relevant, valid psychological events are those which can be observed, i.e. behaviour.

CATATONIC (-IA)   A usually chronic set of symptoms of ignoring environmental stimuli with extreme movement disturbances, such as either holding one pose for long periods of time or the opposite: constant hyperactivity.

CHOLINERGIC   Relates to *acetylcholine* a neurotransmitter—a type of brain chemical—which makes nerves connect to each other.

COGNITIVE (COGNITION)   Knowing/thinking-related thought processes, as opposed to feeling-related or emotional processes.

COGNITIVE (COUNSELLING/BEHAVIOUR THERAPY)   A 'school' of counselling/ therapy based on theories which derive from COGNITIVE theory, i.e. place prime importance on rational thought processes.

CYTOCHROME   A type of protein involved in metabolism. Some (P-450 group) involved with metabolism and elimination of toxins, such as NEUROLEPTIC drugs.

DELUSION   False belief, in simple terms. If it contains threat to self or persecution, then it would be a PARANOID DELUSION.

DISSOCIATION (DISSOCIATIVE)   A fugue, trance-like or altered state where contact with immediate experience is impaired because the person has split or cut off and 'gone away' whilst still remaining conscious. Widely understood as a protective mechanism to block out threatening experiences and/or memories.

EXISTENTIALISM   Relating to the philosophy of existence. A very wide variety of thought within this philosophical tradition, some of it contradicting other parts. As approach to therapy, see Cooper, 2004.

EXPERIENTIAL (COUNSELLING)   Eclectic approach springing from Rogers' and Gendlin's work, incorporating elements of Gestalt therapy (see Baker,

2004 for introduction). Term is also used by Alvin Mahrer to describe his approach.

EXTRATHERAPEUTIC FACTORS   Almost anything outside of therapy, such as the client's personality characteristics, social conditions, economic status, etc.

FLORID   An extravagant and elaborate symptomatology; fully developed, complete example of a syndrome.

FOCUSING (-ORIENTED COUNSELLING)   An approach developed by Eugene Gendlin, one of Carl Rogers' students and colleagues, and based on the inner flow of experience. (See Purton, 2007 for introduction.)

FULLY FUNCTIONING   Congruent, optimal personal development (Rogers, 1959).

GENOTYPING   Scientifically determining the genetic structure of an individual.

GESTALT   German word meaning whole shape or form. Here relates to a 'school' of therapy founded by Fritz Perls.

HOLISTIC   Idea that a system cannot be understood by looking at its constituent parts, only by looking at its integrated, functioning whole.

HUMANISTIC PSYCHOLOGY   A reaction to both BEHAVIOURISM and PSYCHOANALYSIS (and so dubbed the 'third force' in psychology since neither represented the healthy, growthful, creative *person*), founded by, amongst others, Carl Rogers and Abraham Maslow.

IATROGENIC   Effects caused by a medical treatment—most often used to mean a pathological state or illness caused by medical treatment.

IDEATION   The process of forming, or 'having', ideas.

INTERVENTION   Used to mean counsellor/therapist response.

LATENT   An (in psychology) unexpressed ability, or psychological event.

MEDICAL MODEL (OF MENTAL 'ILLNESS')   The system used to understand and classify psychological distress in the Western world. Classification system based on the similarity of symptoms, *not* on cause-and-effect relationships (is *not* a disease model, although it looks like one). It mimics a medical model of physical disease—used by psychiatrists and majority of mental health professionals.

MEMORY ENHANCEMENT/RETRAINING   Programmes for improving memory in head injury and Alzheimer's patients: taught techniques and exercises.

META-ANALYSIS   A comprehensive overview of research studies which aggregates the results to come to a 'grand' or overarching conclusion.

MILIEU   Whole surroundings, environment or setting.

NEUROLEPTIC   AntiPSYCHOTIC drug, also usually tranquillising (sedating).

NEUROLEPTIC MALIGNANT SYNDROME   Illness caused by antiPSYCHOTIC drugs: muscle tremors, rigidity, unstable blood pressure, confusion, coma.

NEUROLOGICAL   Neurology: the science of the nerves and nervous system.

NEUROSIS   Relatively 'mild' psychological/emotional distress, or 'disorder': anxiety, phobia, compulsion, but no 'PSYCHOTIC' symptoms, e.g., DELUSION or hallucination.

OPERATIONALISE In psychology, to outline the steps necessary to put something into operation.

ORGANIC CONDITION/DISEASE A condition or illness with a physical/ biological cause (rather than psychological), e.g. brain tumours are physical (organic) entities but symptoms can in some circumstances look like the symptoms of psychological distress (mood swings). Also, e.g. delirium (hallucinations and DELUSIONS) caused by fever.

OUTCOME (MEASURES) The measure of how a client feels at the end of therapy against an external yardstick (an anxiety or 'adjustment' scale or other PSYCHOMETRIC TEST). Not the same as a 'change status' measure which looks at improvement.

PARANOIA Feelings (often DELUSIONAL) of persecution and threat to self.

PHARMACOLOGY (PSYCHO-) The study of drugs in psychological functioning.

PHENOMENOLOGY Approach to understanding and psychology where 'truth' or 'knowledge' comes from the perceptual field of the individual, rather than an external authority. Based on work of philosopher Edmund Husserl.

PRIMARY PREVENTION RESEARCH Looking at the factors which predispose people to certain conditions/distress, such as social and environmental conditions, and personal characteristics and experiences.

PROZAC Trade name of fluoxetine hydrochloride: a selective serotonin reuptake inhibitor (SSRI) antidepressant.

PSYCHOANALYSIS/PSYCHOANALYTIC 'School' of psychology originated by, and based on, the work of Sigmund Freud.

PSYCHOPATHOLOGY The study or manifestation of mental (psychological) disorder (pathology). A term originating in the medicalisation of distress.

PSYCHOSIS/PSYCHOTIC A MEDICAL-MODEL classification of severe distress characterised by loss of contact with reality and lack of insight (person doesn't think they are 'ill'). Types include SCHIZOPHRENIA, clinical depression, bipolar disorder.

PSYCHOSOCIAL (INTERVENTION) Treatment combining psychological elements and social (family, groupwork, housing, occupational) elements.

PSYCHOTROPIC (Drug) affecting the mind.

QUALITATIVE (RESEARCH METHODS) Concerned with the *qualities* of experience and human behaviour.

QUANTITATIVE (RESEARCH METHODS) Concerned with the *quantities* of experience and human behaviour.

RANDOMISED CONTROLLED TRIALS Patients/clients are randomly (by chance) allocated to one of two groups, one 'treatment' group and one 'control' group. The treatment group receives the treatment under investigation, and the control group receives either no treatment or some standard default treatment.

REDUCTIONISM/REDUCTIONISTIC The method of analysis where the subject under study is broken down into simpler and simpler areas and units. This increasing simplification of a complex subject is based on the idea that complex processes can be entirely explained by looking at their assumed components.

REGRESSED/REGRESSIVE/REGRESSION   Reversion to an early(ier) stage of emotional or psychological development.

RELIABLE/RELIABILITY   Replicability. In research terms the chance of getting the same results again.

REMINISCENCE (THERAPY)   Encouraging the act of reminiscence using photographs, music, smells, tastes, etc.

RESOLUTION (THERAPY)   Focuses on how a person is managing their current situation rather than trying to make sense of past conflicts. Tries to help understand the meaning behind confused behaviours or confused speech.

SAMPLE   A representative group of 'subjects' (people) selected for a study.

SCHIZOPHRENIA   Serious psychological distress or mental 'illness'. Classified in MEDICAL MODEL as 'PSYCHOSIS'. Many very distressing symptoms of confused, chaotic thoughts and feelings, DELUSIONS and hallucinations.

SECTION   Unofficial term for involuntary detention, hospitalisation or other medical treatment under (in the UK) the Mental Health Act 1983 (which has *sections* describing the necessary powers for detention).

SELF-CONCEPT   The view one has of one's self—part of the personality. More fluid in a fully functioning person, more rigid in an incongruent person.

SINGLE-CASE STUDY   A research method which analyses a single example, e.g. one therapist with one client. Usually inappropriate for statistical analysis.

STATISTICAL SIGNIFICANCE   A measure of the probability of something happening by chance. In simple terms it is used to mean that it is a *real* effect.

SUBCEIVE   Subsception: sub-conscious, pre- or out-of-awareness processing of stimuli.

SUPER SENSITIVITY PSYCHOSIS   Illness caused by antiPSYCHOTIC drugs similar to TARDIVE DYSKINESIA. Can be part of NEUROLEPTIC withdrawal symptoms.

SYMBOLISATION   Bringing an experience into conscious awareness and giving it meaning. So pre-symbolic experience would be an experience which either is not yet in awareness and/or has no fully developed meaning.

TARDIVE DYSKINESIA   Permanent neurological condition caused by NEUROLEPTIC drugs. Parkinson-like involuntary movements/shaking fingers, feet, legs, head, lolling tongue and internal agitation/restlessness.

TARDIVE PSYCHOSIS   See SUPER SENSITIVITY PSYCHOSIS. Term more often used to refer to symptoms after withdrawal from NEUROLEPTIC medication.

TITRATE   Term originally from chemistry. Here used to mean process of prescribing the absolute minimum dosage of drugs to have therapeutic effect whilst minimising 'side' effects.

VALIDATION THERAPY   For disorientated very old people; involves validating experiences of aging and resolution of unfinished life business.

VALIDITY   Of a measuring instrument: does it measure what it claims to measure?

REFERENCES

Baker, N (2004) Experiential person-centred therapy. In P Sanders (ed) *The Tribes of the Person-centred Nation* (pp. 67–94) Ross-on-Wye: PCCS Books.

Bowlby, J (1953/65) *Child Care and the Growth of Love*. Harmondsworth: Pelican.

Buber, M (1958) *I and Thou*. Edinburgh: T and T Clark.

Buber, M (1964) Elements of the interhuman. In M Friedman *The Worlds of Existentialism* (pp. 229, 547). New York: Random House.

Cameron, R (2003) Psychological contact (Chapters 7 & 8). In J Tolan *Skills in Person-Centred Counselling and Psychotherapy* (pp. 87–109). London: Sage.

Cooper, M (2004) Existential approaches to therapy. In P Sanders (ed) *The Tribes of the Person-Centred Nation* (pp. 95–124). Ross-on-Wye: PCCS Books.

Davies, N & Burdett, J (2004) Preventing 'schizophrenia': Creating the conditions for saner societies. In J Read, LR Mosher & RP Bentall (eds) *Models of Madness: Psychological, social and biological approaches to schizophrenia* (pp. 271–82)*. London: Routledge.

Dekeyser, M, Prouty, GF & Elliott, R (in press) Pre-Therapy process and outcome: A review of research instruments and results. *Person-Centered and Experiential Psychotherapies*.

Deleu, C & Van Werde, D (1998) The relevance of a phenomenological attitude when working with psychotic people. In B Thorne & E Lambers (eds) *Person-Centred Therapy: A European perspective* (pp. 206–15). London: Sage.

Dinacci, A (1997) Ricerca sperimentale sul trattamento psicologico dei pazienti schizophrenici con la pre-therapia di Dr G Prouty. *Psicologia della Persona, 2*, 4, 7–16.

Dodds, P, Morton,I, & Prouty, G (2004) Pre-Therapy and Dementia. *Journal of Dementia Care, 12*, 2, 25–7.

Embleton Tudor, L, Keemar, K, Tudor, K, Valentine, J, & Worrall, M (2004) *The Person-Centred Approach: A contemporary introduction*. Basingstoke: Palgrave.

Feil, N (1993) *The Validation Breakthrough: Simple techniques for communicating with people with Alzheimer's type dementia*. London: Health Professions Press.

Freeth, R (2007) *Humanising Psychiatry and Mental Health Care*. Oxford: Radcliffe.

Gendlin, ET (1964) A theory of personality change. In P Worchel & D Byrne (eds) *Personality Change*, New York: Wiley.

Gendlin, ET (1973) Experiential psychotherapy. In R Corsini (ed) *Current Psychotherapies* (pp. 317–52). Itasca: FE Peacock.

Goldsmith, M (1996) *Hearing the Voice of People with Dementia*. London: Jessica Kingsley.

Hansebo, G & Kihlgren, M (2002) Carers' interactions with patients suffering from severe dementia: A difficult balance to facilitate mutual togetherness. *Journal of Clinical Nursing, 1*, 2, 225–36.

Harlow, HF (1959) Love in infant monkeys. *Scientific American*, 200, 68–74.

Hinterkopf, E, Prouty, G & Brunswick, L (1979) A pilot study of Pre-Therapy method applied to chronic schizophrenic patients. *Psychosocial Rehabilitation Journal, 3*, 11–19.

Innes, A, MacPherson S & McCabe, L (2006) *Promoting Person-Centred Care at *the Front Line*. York: Joseph Rowntree Foundation.

Keady, J (2006) *Partnerships in Community Mental Health Nursing and Dementia Care*. Buckingham: Open University Press.

Killick, J (2002) Creativity and dementia: 'Holding a rainbow in our hands'. Text of Presentation http://www.dementia.com.au/papers_2002/ John_Killick_Creativity_and_Dementia. (Accessed 30/9/03.)

Killick, J (2005) Making sense of dementia through metaphor. *Journal of Dementia Care*, 13, 1, 22–3.

Killick, J & Allan, K (2001) *Communication and the Care of People with Dementia*. Buckingham: Open University Press.

Kitwood, T (1997) *Dementia Reconsidered: The person comes first*. Buckingham: Open University Press.

Kirschenbaum, H & Henderson, VL (1990) *The Carl Rogers Reader*. London: Constable.

Kontos, PC (2005) Embodied selfhood in Alzheimer's Disease. *Dementia, 4*, 4, 553–70.

Krietemeyer, B & Prouty, G (2003) The art of psychological contact: The psychotherapy of a retarded psychotic client. *Person-Centered & Experiential Psychotherapies, 2*, 3, 151–61.

Lea, M & Spears, R (1995) Love at first byte?: Building personal relationships over computer networks. In JT Wood & S Duck (eds) *Under-studied relationships: Off the beaten track*. Thousand Oaks, CA: Sage.

McCormack, B (2004) Person-centredness in gerontological nursing: An overview of the literature. *International Journal of Older People Nursing, 13*, 31–8.

Morton, I (1996) Beyond validation. In. IJ Norman and SJ Redfern (eds). *Mental Health Care for Elderly People*. London: Churchill Livingstone.

Murphy, LJ & Mitchell, DL (1998) When writing helps to heal: E-mail as therapy. *British Journal of Guidance and Counselling, 26*, 1, 21–32.

Perls, F (1969) *Ego, Hunger and Aggression: A revision of Freud's theory and method*. New York: Vintage Books.

Pörtner, M (1990) Client-centered therapy with mentally retarded persons: Catherine and Ruth. In G Lietaer, J Rombauts, R Van Balen (eds) *Client-Centered and Experiential Psychotherapy in the Nineties* (pp. 659–69). Leuven: Leuven University Press.

Pörtner, M (2000/2007) *Trust and Understanding: The person-centered approach in everyday care for people with special needs*. Ross-on-Wye: PCCS Books. Second, revised and extended edition (2007). Original German edition (1996). *Ernstnehmen, Zutrauen, Verstehen: Personzentrierte Haltung im Umgang mit geistig behinderten und pflegebedürftigen Menschen*. Stuttgart: Klett-Cotta. 4th revised and extended edition (2004).

Pörtner, M (2002) Psychotherapy for people with special needs: A challenge for client-centered psychotherapists. In JC Watson, RN Goldman, & MS Warner (eds) *Client-Centered and Experiential Psychotherapy in the 21st Century: Advances in theory, research and practice* (pp. 380–6). Ross-on-Wye: PCCS Books.

Pörtner, M (2003/2007) *Brücken bauen. Menschen mit geistiger Behinderung verstehen und begleiten*. Second revised and extended edition (2007). Stuttgart:

Klett-Cotta.

Pörtner, M (in press). Pre-therapeutic approaches with people with special needs. In G Prouty (ed) *Emergent Developments in Pre-Therapy*. Ross-on-Wye: PCCS Books.

Prouty, GF (1994) *Theoretical Evolutions in Person-Centered/Experiential Therapy: Applications to schizophrenic and retarded psychoses*. Westport: Praeger.

Prouty, GF (1998) Pre-Therapy and the pre-expressive self. *Person-Centred Practice*, 6, 2, 80–8.

Prouty, GF (2001) Humanistic psychotherapy for people with schizophrenia. In DJ Cain and J Seeman (eds) *Humanistic Psychotherapies: Handbook of research and practice* (pp. 579–601). Washington, DC: American Psychological Association.

Prouty, GF & Cronwall M (1990) Psychotherapy with a depressed mentally retarded adult: An application of Pre-Therapy. In A Dosen & F Menolascino (eds) *Depression in Mentally Retarded Children and Adults* (pp. 281–93). Leiden: Logon Publicaties.

Prouty, GF, Van Werde, D & Pörtner, M (2002) *Pre-Therapy: Reaching contact-impaired clients*. Ross-on-Wye: PCCS Books. Original German edition (1998) *Prä-Therapie*. Stuttgart: Klett-Cotta.

Prouty, G & Van Werde, D (in press) Student-centered supervision of Pre-Therapy. In K Tudor & M Worrall (eds) *Freedon to Practice II: Person-centred approaches to supervision*. Ross-on-Wye: PCCS Books.

Purton, C (2007) *The Focusing-Oriented Counselling Primer*. Ross-on-Wye: PCCS Books.

Rabins, PV, Lyketsos, CG & Steele CD (2006) *Practical Dementia Care*. Oxford: Oxford University Press.

Roelens, L (1994) Foreword. In G Prouty *Theoretical Evolutions in Person-Centered/Experiential Therapy: Applications to schizophrenic and retarded psychoses* (pp. xi–xxii). Westport: Praeger.

Rogers, CR (1951) *Client-Centered Therapy*. Boston: Houghton Mifflin.

Rogers, CR (1957) The necessary and sufficient conditions of therapeutic personality change. *Journal of Consulting Psychology, 21,* 95–103. Reprinted in H Kirschenbaum & VL Henderson (eds) (1990) *The Carl Rogers Reader* (pp. 219–35). London: Constable.

Rogers, CR (1959) A theory of therapy, personality and interpersonal relationships, as developed in the client-centered framework. In S Koch (ed) *Psychology: A study of science, Vol. 3: Formulations of the person and the social context* (pp. 184–256). New York: McGraw-Hill.

Rogers, CR, Gendlin, ET, Kiesler, DJ and Truax, CB (1967) *The Therapeutic Relationship and its Impact: A study of psychotherapy with schizophrenics*. Madison: University of Wisconsin Press.

Sanders, P (2006) *The Person-Centred Counselling Primer*. Ross-on-Wye: PCCS Books.

Shlien, JM (1961/2003) A client-centered approach to schizophrenia: A first approximation. In A Burton (ed) *Psychotherapy of the Psychoses* (pp. 285–317). New York: Basic Books. Reprinted in JM Shlien (2003) *To Lead an*

Honorable Life (pp. 30–59). Ross-on-Wye: PCCS Books.

Sommerbeck, L (2003) *The Client-Centred Therapist in Psychiatric Contexts: A therapists' guide to the psychiatric landscape and its inhabitants.* Ross-on-Wye: PCCS Books.

Stamatiadis, R (1990/2002) Sharing life therapy. *Person-Centered Review, 5,* 287–307. Reprinted in G Wyatt & P Sanders (2002) (eds) *Rogers' Therapeutic Conditions. Volume 4: Contact and Perception* (pp. 274–87). Ross-on-Wye: PCCS Books.

Stern, DN (1985) *The Interpersonal World of the Infant: A view from psychoanalysis and developmental psychology.* London: Karnac Books.

Thorne, B (1985/1991) *The Quality of Tenderness.* Norwich: Norwich Centre Publications. Reprinted in B Thorne (1991) *Person-Centred Counselling: Therapeutic and spiritual dimensions* (pp. 73–81). London: Whurr.

Tudor, K (2000) The case of the lost conditions. *Counselling, 11,* 1, 33–7.

Van Werde, D (2002a) A contact milieu. In G Prouty, D Van Werde and M Pörtner *Pre-Therapy: Reaching contact-impaired clients* (pp. 77–114). Ross-on-Wye: PCCS Books.

Van Werde, D (2002b) Prouty's Pre-Therapy and contact-work with a broad range of persons' pre-expressive functioning. In G Wyatt & P Sanders (eds) *Rogers' Therapeutic Conditions: Volume 4: Contact and Perception* (pp. 168–81). Ross-on-Wye: PCCS Books.

Van Werde, D (2005) Facing psychotic functioning: Person-centred contact work in residential psychiatric care. In S Joseph & R Worsley, (eds): *Person-Centred Psychopathology: A positive psychology of mental health* (pp. 158–68). Ross-on-Wye: PCCS Books.

Van Werde, D & Morton, I (1999) The relevance of Prouty's Pre-Therapy to dementia care. In I Morton (ed) *Person-Centred Approaches to Dementia Care* (pp. 139–66). Bicester: Winslow Press.

Van Werde, D, & Prouty, G (2007) Pre-Therapy: Empathic contact with individuals at pre-expressive levels of functioning. In M Cooper, P Schmid, M O'Hara & G Wyatt (eds) *The Handbook of Person-Centered Therapy* (pp. 237–50). Basingstoke: Palgrave.

Warner, MS (2002) Psychological contact, meaningful process and human nature. In G Wyatt and P Sanders (eds) *Rogers' Therapeutic Conditions, Volume. 4: Contact and Perception* (pp. 76–95). Ross-on-Wye: PCCS Books.

Whelton, W & Greenberg, LS (2002) Psychological contact as dialectical construction. In G Wyatt and P Sanders (eds) *Rogers' Therapeutic Conditions, Volume 4: Contact and Perception* (pp. 96–114). Ross-on-Wye: PCCS Books.

World Health Organisation (1992) *The ICD-10 Classification of Mental and Behavioural Disorders: Clinical descriptions and diagnostic guidelines.* Geneva: WHO.

Worsley, R (2004) Integrating with integrity. In P Sanders (ed) *The Tribes of the Person-Centred Nation: An introduction to the schools of therapy associated with the person-centred approach* (pp. 125–48). Ross-on-Wye: PCCS Books.

Wyatt, G & Sanders, P (eds) (2002) *Rogers' Therapeutic Conditions. Volume 4: Contact and Perception.* Ross-on-Wye: PCCS Books.

INDEX